READING
Triumphs

Practice Book

Program Authors

Dr. Jan E. Hasbrouck
Educational Consultant
J. H. Consulting
Seattle, Washington

Dr. Janice A. Dole
University of Utah
Salt Lake City, Utah

Mc Graw Hill Macmillan McGraw-Hill

D1288497

Contents

Unit 2   Discoveries

Unit 3   Turning Points

Unit 4   Experiences

© Macmillan/McGraw-Hill

Unit 5 Achievements

Unit 6 Great Ideas

Name _____

The vowel sound is short in words such as *cat, red, sit, hop,* and *run.*

A. Underline the short vowels in the words below.

| bump | slips | sip | jump | miss |
| luck | tug | pals | lamp | last |

B. Read the clues. Then use the words to complete the sentences.

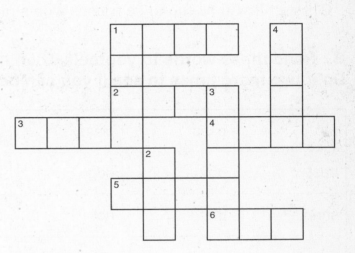

Across

1. Before the game, my mom said, "Good __."

2. In the winter, I __ spring.

3. After I fell I had a __ on my leg.

4. Jon ran slowly and came in __.

5. I like to __ off my bed!

6. When my drink is hot, I take a __.

Down

1. If it is dark, Meg turns on a __.

2. If the door is stuck, just give it a __.

3. When it is icy, Len always __.

4. Jon and Jay are best __.

A. As you read, pay attention to pauses, stops and intonation.

	Dan likes to rap. He raps as he passes in the hall. He raps on his
15	trip home from class. Dan's friends like how well Dan raps.
27	Dan rapped in a contest. He was the best! Now he will rap on
41	*American Rap Star*! It is a contest on TV!
50	Dan is on edge. He is worried that he will not rap well. Can his
65	friends help him? Will he rap on TV? If Dan raps on TV he will be a
81	star. It will be fun to be friends with a rap star. 94

B. Read these words to yourself. Then have your partner time you. Do it two more times to see if you can beat your score!

rap	pass	class	cop	hat
best	on	edge	how	well
snap	that	not	trip	hop
help	clip	drop	Dan	fat
grip	will	flop	rat	pop

Record Your Scores

Time 1: _____   Time 2: _____   Time 3: _____

At Home: Read the passage again. Then write two sentences using the words above. Read them aloud.

Name _____

Add *-ed*, *-s*, *-es*, or *-ing* to the end of a word to change the meaning.

A. Fill in the missing parts to make the word in bold.

1. We **camped** out by the tree.

camp + _____ **= camped**

2. The mother **kissed** her baby.

_____ **+** _____ **= kissed**

3. Pat **walks** fast.

_____ **+** _____ **=** _____

4. I have **glasses** in my desk.

_____ **+** _____ **=** _____

5. Ted is **running** home.

_____ **+** _____ **+** _____ **= running**

B. Write two sentences about friends. Use the word *hugged* in one sentence. Use the word *talking* in the other.

1. _____

_____

2. _____

_____

A. Vocabulary Words Check *true* or *false* for each statement.

1. If you get lost, you might be worried.   ☐true ☐false

2. If you are nervous you will feel relaxed.   ☐true ☐false

3. People usually wear a shoe on each hand.   ☐true ☐false

4. She slips when the sidewalk is dry.   ☐true ☐false

5. You might be on edge if you have a big test.   ☐true ☐false

B. Vocabulary Strategy: Context Clues Underline the context clues that help you figure out each bold-faced word.

Mary is going to ice skate. Her body feels tense because she is **on edge**. It is her first time on ice skates. If she **slips** she might fall. She is **worried** about getting hurt. Her mom holds her hand. When Mary steps onto the ice she opens her mouth, takes in a big gulp of air, and **gasps**. She did not even fall! Mary lets go of her mom's hand. She can do it! Look at Mary go! She didn't have to be so **nervous**!

Which three vocabulary words have almost the same meaning?

_____   _____   _____

Name _____

After reading "Dan Can Rap," make a list of the story's characters in the first column of the Character and Plot Chart. Write about the plot of the story in the second column.

Characters	Plot

Name _____

Read the passage. Then complete the questions.

In Step!

Classes are gathered in the gym for a step contest. They were astonished by what they saw. The first team amazed the crowd! "I'm surprised," said Val, "They are really good." Val, Jen, and Shannon are a team. Shannon watches how well others can step. She is on edge. She is worried she will mess up. There is so much suspense in the air!

Jen begins. Shannon and Val join in. They clap, step, and spin.

Then, Jen slips! The crowd gasps. Kids gather around Jen. She is hurt.

A girl named Lin comes over. "I know the steps."

"Go!" cries Jen. "We can win!"

Shannon is nervous. Lin begins the steps again. Lin is good at stepping! They step, stomp, and spin as a team.

Jen has a big grin. "We did win!"

1. Underline words in the passage that have short vowel sounds.

2. Circle the words in the passage with inflectional endings.

3. Who are the characters in the story?

   _____

4. What happens at the end of the story?

   _____

5. Jen might clap, or give the team a _____ for a good job.
   hand   band   hold

At Home: Reread the passage and talk about your favorite part of the story.

Name _____

A silent *e* at the end of a word can make the vowel say its name.

A. Underline the long vowels in the words below.

kite   lake   cone   cute   time

rake   pole   plate   mine   hope

B. Read the clues. Then use the above words to complete the crossword puzzle.

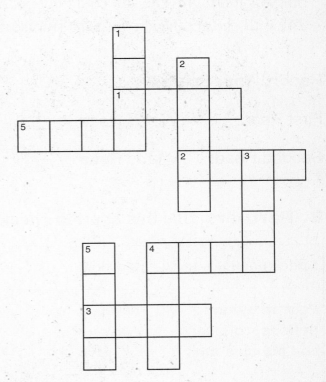

Across

1. A stop sign sits on top of a __.

2. A clock can tell you the __.

3. Cass ran, holding the string of her __.

4. Stan ate ice cream on a __.

5. Fran made a pile of leaves with a __.

Down

1. Bob used a __ to tie up the box.

2. Jill set a hot dog on the __.

3. That book is __.

4. I think Rob has a __ dog.

5. The catfish swam in the __.

Name _____

**A. Have a partner time you as you read the passage.
Record your scores below.**

12	Paul Bunyan liked his logging job. He could cut 400 trees a day by himself. He stood a mile high!
20	He let his kid, Jane, help dig and plant trees. She was a big girl,
35	too. Jane was three states long and as wide as a Great Lake!
48	One day, Paul and his friends made a cabin. The smokestack
59	was too high! The sun could not get by. What will Jane do to help?
74	Will she get the sun past the smokestack? 82

Record Your Scores

First Read: Words Read _____   Time _____

Second Read: Words Read _____   Time _____

B. Partners Use this chart to check your partner's reading.

Speed	☐ too slow	☐ too fast	☐ just right
Paid attention to periods, commas, end punctuation	☐ never	☐ sometimes	☐ always
Accuracy	☐ skipped words	☐ self-corrected	☐ read every word
Read with feeling	☐ never	☐ sometimes	☐ always

© Macmillan/McGraw-Hill

At Home: Reread the passage and talk about
Paul's problem.

Name _____

Add *-ed*, *-s*, *-es*, and *-ing* to a word to change the meaning. If the root word ends in an e, y, or a consonant after a short vowel, change it before the ending is added.

A. Which word is correct? Write it on the line. Put a (/) in front of the ending.

Example

| makeing | making | *mak/ing* |

1. pickked   picked   _____

2. driving   driveing   _____

3. grabbed   grabed   _____

4. poking   pokeing   _____

5. worryed   worried   _____

B. Combine the words to make a compound word.

1. time   bed   _____

2. dust   pan   _____

3. hand   bag   _____

4. sick   home   _____

5. side   in   _____

Name _____

| create | logging | awoke | enormous | smokestack |

A. Vocabulary Words: Check *true* or *false* for each statement.

1. You can **create** a fire from sticks and a match. ☐ true ☐ false

2. Saws are never used in **logging**. ☐ true ☐ false

3. Sara **awoke** from a long nap. ☐ true ☐ false

4. A mouse is an **enormous** animal. ☐ true ☐ false

5. A **smokestack** sits on top of a house. ☐ true ☐ false

6. Which would be **enormous**? Tell why below.
   a. an elephant   **b.** a chicken

   _____

   _____

B. Vocabulary Strategy: Compound Words Match the compound word on the left with its meaning on the right. Draw a line from the word to its meaning.

1. firefly   **a.** the time of day between noon and night

2. cupcake   **b.** a game played with a bat, ball, and bases

3. afternoon   **c.** a small cake

4. baseball   **d.** a pipe that smoke goes up through

5. smokestack   **e.** a flying insect that makes flashes of light

Name _____

As you reread "Jane Wins a Job," describe the setting in the first column of the Plot and Setting Chart. Then write about the plot in the second column.

Setting	Plot

Name _____

Read the passage. Then complete the questions.

Paul's Ox

Paul Bunyan had an ox named Babe. She was huge just like Paul and Jane. She could eat thirty bales of hay as a snack! It took a blackbird a full day to fly from one of Babe's horns to the other.

One time, Paul awoke and found that two ice storms had hit his land. It was so cold that his hot drink froze! On his notepad he wrote that Babe would need new shoes to keep warm.

Zeke was the blacksmith for the logging camp. He lived in a huge cabin with an iron smokestack. He was the only man who could put shoes on Babe. If Babe needed new shoes they had to open a new iron mine to create them. One time Zeke was taking a set of shoes to Babe. They were so enormous that he felt his legs sinking into the mud with each step! This time the land was so cold that he would not sink. Babe would get her shoes and Zeke would be fine.

1. Underline words in the passage that contain silent *e*.

2. Circle the compound words in the passage.

3. Where does the story take place?

_____

4. What happened to Paul's hot drink?

_____

5. If you chop down a tree, you are _____.

          singing   logging   treeing

At Home: Reread the story and talk about Babe's problem.

© Macmillan/McGraw-Hill

Name _____

Read the passage. Then complete the questions.

Ben and Jack Stop Drumming

Ben drums well. Jack drums well. Ben and Jack are best friends.

One day, Miss Grand tells Ben and Jack that there will be a contest. She will pick the best kid to drum in the band. She will pick Ben or Jack.

Ben drums on his books. Jack drums on the bus. Ben drums on his desk. Jack drums as he goes down the hall. There is too much drumming!

So, Miss Grand says, "Stop! I will pick both Ben and Jack to be in the band. Just stop drumming!"

In the end, Ben and Jack both win the contest!

This is a character in the passage.

This is a signal word.

1. Underline the following signal words or phrases in the passage:
   one day   so   in the end

2. Put a box around the names of the three characters in the passage.

3. On the lines below, tell the plot of this story in two sentences.

_____

_____

_____

_____

Name _____

Read the passage. Then complete the questions.

Bill's Bride

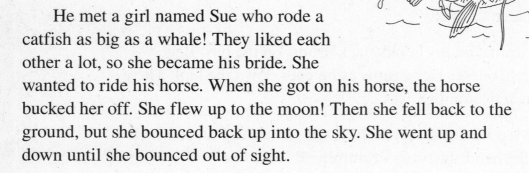

Pecos Bill was a cowboy out west.
When he was a kid he played with bears.
He rode a big cat, called a cougar. He
snapped a rattlesnake as a whip!

He met a girl named Sue who rode a
catfish as big as a whale! They liked each
other a lot, so she became his bride. She
wanted to ride his horse. When she got on his horse, the horse
bucked her off. She flew up to the moon! Then she fell back to the
ground, but she bounced back up into the sky. She went up and
down until she bounced out of sight.

1. Underline the following signal words in the passage:
   when   then   so

2. Put a box around the setting of the passage.

3. Add an ending to the plot of the story. Tell what you think
   Pecos Bill does when Sue bounces out of sight.

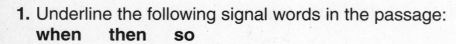

_____

_____

Name _____

> **Consonant digraphs** are two consonants together that make one sound, such as *sh, th, wh*, and *ph*.

A. Underline the consonant digraphs in the words below.

shame	whine	shake	shed	whale
phone	thin	cash	bathe	elephant

B. Circle each word in the puzzle. Look for the consonant digraphs to help you.

t	e	l	e	p	h	a	n	t
h	w	h	a	l	e	b	c	s
i	l	a	t	e	e	a	a	h
n	s	h	a	k	e	t	s	a
e	h	b	h	p	a	h	h	m
v	e	w	h	i	n	e	w	e
k	d	p	h	o	n	e	d	p

C. Use the correct words from above to complete each sentence.

1. An __ __ __ __ __|__|__ __ is a big, gray animal.

2. Rattles are fun to __ __ __|__|__.

3. You use __ __|__|__ to buy things.

4. Call me on the __ __ __|__|__.

Write the letters from the boxes above to spell a secret message!

A __ __ __ __e sheds its skin.
   3 4 1 2

© Macmillan/McGraw-Hill

Name _____

A. As you read, pay attention to word accuracy.

11 | When you think about snakes you might shudder and shake. If
26 | you see a snake, you might wish to run! But not all snakes bite or
42 | squeeze their prey. If you will be hiking or if you plan to be by a
54 | swamp, you can learn about snakes and reptiles before you go. Or
68 | you can find photos on a website of snakes you might see on your
83 | trek. Stay on a path when you hike. Hike with a friend. Put on thick
95 | socks and boots a snake cannot bite through. Be safe and have fun. 96

B. Read these words. Then have a partner time you.
Do it two more times to see if you can beat your score!

shudder	path	phone	can	pal
photos	other	thick	dish	tell
what	through	think	get	prey
shake	that	wish	red	run
with	when	their	put	socks

Record Your Scores

Time 1: _____   Time 2: _____   Time 3: _____

© Macmillan/McGraw-Hill

At Home: Reread the passage aloud and talk about what you know about snakes.

Name _____

A **closed syllable** ends in a consonant. Most closed syllables have a short vowel sound.

A. Fill in the missing parts to make the bold-faced word.

1. The **kitten** likes to hit the ball.

   kit + _____ **= kitten**

2. Our team won the **contest**.

   con + _____ **= contest**

3. That car is small and **compact**.

   com+ _____ **= compact**

4. The **sunset** was pretty.

   sun + _____ **= sunset**

5. What is your **address**?

   ad + _____ **= address**

B. Write two sentences about a park or playground. Use the word *happen* **in one sentence. Use the word** *insect* **in the other.**

1. _____

   _____

2. _____

   _____

Name _____

| reptile | prey | venom | stun | victim |

A. Vocabulary Words: Cloze Paragraph Use the correct word from above to complete each sentence.

A snake is a **1.** _____. Many snakes **2.** _____

on mice and rats. Some snakes have **3.** _____ that they use

to **4.** _____ or kill their prey. Then the snake will swallow

its **5.** _____ whole. They are interesting creatures.

B. Vocabulary Strategy: Homographs Use this dictionary entry to answer the questions that follow.

1. What is the first definition for the word "wind"?

_____

2. What is another definition for the word "wind"?

_____

_____

wind/wind

wind (wĭnd), [*n*]. **1.** a movement of air
wind (wīnd), [*v*]. **1.** to wrap around
    something. **2.** to move in a twisting
    way

3. Can you think of another word that has the same vowel sound as the one you hear in the first "wind"? How about a word with the same vowel sound as the one you hear in the second "wind"?

_____

_____

Name _____

Read "Do They Make You Shudder and Shake?" Then, use the Venn
Diagram to compare and contrast the information in the selection.

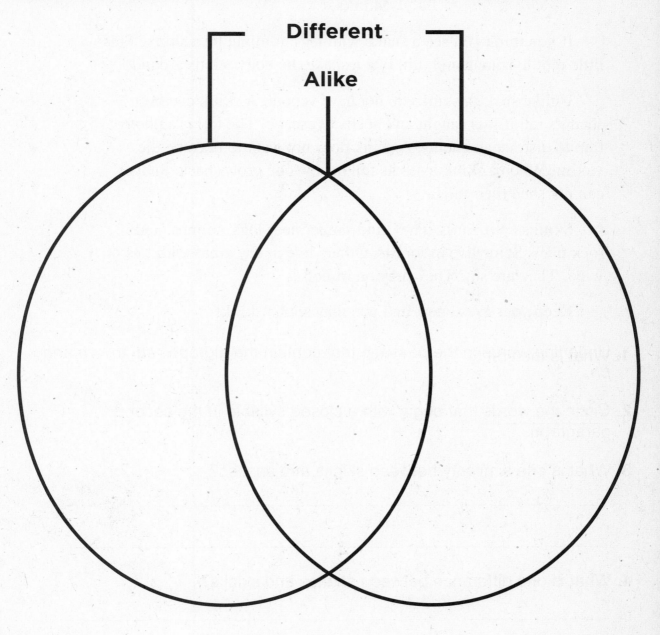

Different

Alike

Read the passage. Then complete the questions.

Skinks

If you think you see a snake with legs, it might be a skink. This little reptile is long and thin like a snake. Its body winds around.

Unlike snakes, skinks do not have venom. A skink can even shed its tail if it is caught and needs to escape! The tail is a phony trap to distract an enemy. A skink does not want to become the victim! When a skink loses its tail, a new one grows back. Snakes can not shed their tails.

Skinks are lizards. They find shelter near logs, stumps, and rock piles. Some live in forests. Others live in dry areas with lots of wind. They are shy. They prey on insects.

Keep your eyes open, and you may spot a skink!

1. Underline words in the passage that contain the digraphs *sh, th, wh* and *ph*.

2. Circle the words that begin with a closed syllable in the second paragraph.

3. What is one similarity between skinks and snakes?

_____

_____

4. What is one difference between snakes and skinks?

_____

_____

5. A skink is a kind of _____.
   mammal   bird   reptile

At Home: Reread the passage and talk about what you learned about skinks.

Name _____

The letters *e, ee,* and *ea* can all stand for the long *e* sound.

A. **Circle the word that best completes each sentence.**
Write the word on the line.

1. When I dance, I move my _____.
feet   felt   fur

2. Jill likes to hear a song with a fast _____.
bun   been   beat

3. Mick looks both ways before he crosses the _____.
steep   street   storm

4. To open the lock, _____ used a key.
she   bee   see

5. Lunch is my favorite _____ of the day.
mint   meal   me

6. Kate likes _____ with every meal.
seats   dreams   beans

7. The baby is just beginning to get _____.
teeth   sheet   read

8. Mike has to _____ his dog before school each day.
green   feed   deep

B. **Find the long *e* sounds in the answer choices above.**
Then underline them.

Name _____

**A. Have a partner time you as you read the passage.
Record your scores below.**

	We can see Mars from right here on planet Earth. Mars is also
13	called the Red Planet because we can see its red dust gleam. But
26	Mars is not all red. It has land much like Earth. It has rocks, and
41	even a volcano!
44	A day on Earth is almost as long as on Mars. That means that
58	Mars spins as fast as Earth. But a year on Mars is almost twice
72	as long as an Earth year. That is how long it needs to orbit the
87	sun. 88

Record Your Scores

First Read: Words Read _____   Time _____

Second Read: Words Read _____   Time _____

B. Partners Use this chart to check your partner's reading.

Speed	☐ too slow	☐ too fast	☐ just right
Paid attention to periods, commas, end punctuation	☐ never	☐ sometimes	☐ always
Accuracy	☐ skipped words	☐ self-corrected	☐ read every word
Read with feeling	☐ never	☐ sometimes	☐ always

© Macmillan/McGraw-Hill

At Home: Reread this passage aloud to a family member and talk about what you know about Mars.

Name _____

A **prefix** is a group of letters added to the front of a word to change its meaning. Most prefixes have more than one meaning.

A. **Fill in the missing parts to make the bold-faced word.**

1. I need to **repack** my bag.

   re + _____ **= repack**

2. Please **untie** your shoes.

   _____ **+ tie =** _____

3. Did you **rewind** the tape?

   _____ **+** _____ **= rewind**

4. I am **unhappy** about the score of the game!

   _____ **+** _____ **=** _____

5. The buttons on his jacket came **undone**.

   _____ **+** _____ **=** _____

B. **Write two sentences about your bedroom. Use the word** *rehang* **in one sentence. Use the word** *undone* **in the other.**

1. _____

   _____

2. _____

   _____

| orbits | object | volcano | gravity |

A. Vocabulary Words: Choose the correct word from above to complete each statement.

Example:

Neat is to *messy* as *smooth* is to ___rumpled___.

1. *Wheel* is to *spins* as *planet* is to _____.

2. *Rain* is to *cloud* as *lava* is to _____.

3. *Float* is to *life jacket* as *fall* is to _____.

B. Vocabulary Strategy: Context Clues Underline the context clues that help you figure out each bold-faced word.

It was the day of the Science Fair. Three projects won ribbons. Jon's project was a 3-D picture of space. He used everyday things, or **objects**, to stand for the planets. He showed how the earth **orbits** the sun by moving a golf ball around a big orange. Sam made his very own **volcano** with brown clay. He used red clay to show the lava coming out, and dry ice for gas. Jenny's project proved that **gravity** pulls things down to the ground. She dropped things like pencils, balls, and feathers. Everyone at the Science Fair did a great job!

Use the correct bold-faced word from above to complete each sentence.

1. If a _____ erupts, hot lava and smoke pour out.

2. You almost float on the moon because there is very little _____.

3. Pens and books are two _____ used in school.

© Macmillan/McGraw-Hill

Name _____

Use the Summary Chart to summarize the story "Seeing Mars."

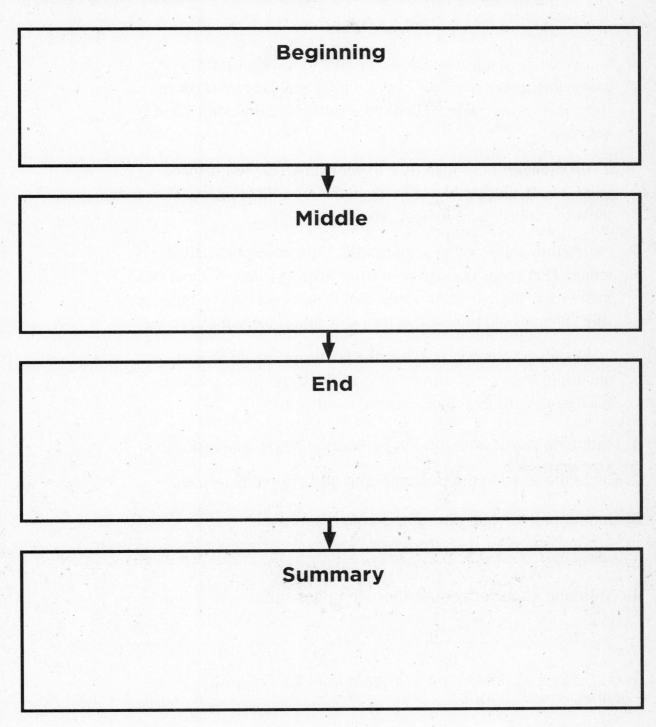

Beginning

Middle

End

Summary

Read the passage. Then complete the questions.

Space Walk

What do you think it would be like to walk in space? For astronauts, a space walk is both exciting and dangerous. In space, there is no gravity. Planets orbit the sun. There are craters and volcanos.

Astronauts must take time to get ready. They wear space suits. These suits protect them from the icy cold of space. They help the astronauts breathe and talk.

Before going out on a spacewalk, the astronaut checks their tether. This keeps the astronaut from floating away. Without this metal rope, the astronaut would be unable to get back to the space-ship. They would tumble and turn and do a somersault in space.

Safely attached to the ship, the astronaut can do almost anything. A group of astronauts even fixed the space telescope. Each of their tools and objects had a tether, too!

1. Underline words with the long *e* sound spelled *e*, *ee*, or *ea*.

2. Circle the word in the passage that has the prefix *un-*.

3. Summarize the last paragraph in one sentence.

_____

4. Write one important detail about the passage.

_____

5. A _____ keeps the astronaut from floating away.
   tether   suit   tool

© Macmillan/McGraw-Hill

At Home: Reread the passage then talk about walking in space.

Name _____

The letters *a, ai,* and *ay* can stand for the long *a* sound.

A. **Circle the word that best completes each sentence.**
Write the word on the line.

1. When a dog is happy, it will shake its _____.
   tape   tail   tray

2. It was raining, so I did not go out to _____.
   plain   plane   play

3. Gail wailed when she didn't get any letters in the _____.
   may   mall   mail

4. April brushed her ponytail and put it in a _____.
   braid   brad   brain

5. If you want to see a play that is not free, you must _____.
   pray   pay   pain

6. Jaime put on bug _____ before going outside.
   stay   spray   Sunday

7. Jay would only eat a hot dog if it was _____.
   plain   pail   plate

8. Adrian did not like to use crayons, but he did like to use _____.
   trail   hallway   paint

B. **Go back and underline the *ai* and *ay* patterns in the answer**
choices above.

Name _____

A. Use this passage for a choral reading or Readers Theater.

Instructions

	Thank you for helping us train our rescue dogs. You're going to
12	be a big hit as a victim!
19	We will bury you in a snow cave about three feet deep. The
32	dog will find your smell and dig an air hole for you. As you wait to
48	be found, follow these instructions:
53	1) Lie still near your supplies.
58	2) Don't scream, because then the dog will find you by sound
69	and not by smell.
73	3) Don't lose your radio. Keep it close at all times.
83	4) When you see a paw and a nose, hand the rescue dog a treat.
97	5) If you feel really uncomfortable, send us a plea for help on
109	your radio. We will dig you out without waiting for the dog. 121

B. Read these silly sentences aloud. Pause when you see (/) and stop when you see (//). Change your voice when you see a question mark (?) or an exclamation point (!).

1. A quail/ rides a train/ with a snail/ on its tail!//

2. Wait!// My mail/ just dropped/ in the drain!//

3. Can May/ paint my braid?// She can take/ my pail.//

4. I wailed in pain.// In what way/ did I fail?//

5. My brain/ is gray/ and made/ of clay.//

© Macmillan/McGraw-Hill

At Home: Take turns rereading the passage. Did you understand the instructions or would you have any questions if you had to follow them?.

Name _____

A **prefix** is a group of letters added to the front of a word to change its meaning. Most prefixes have more than one meaning.

A. What word can be formed from combining the word parts in each row? Write the word on the line.

Example:

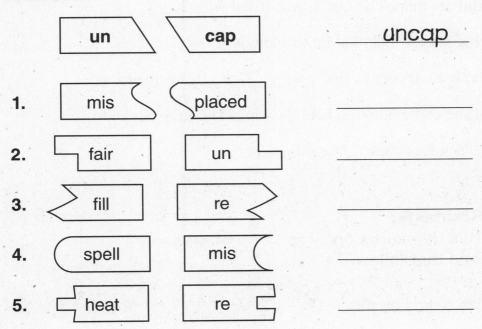

un \ / cap   _uncap_

1.   mis) (placed   _____

2.   fair   un   _____

3.   fill   re   _____

4.   spell   mis   _____

5.   heat   re   _____

B. Use the correct word from above to complete each sentence.

1. If Kay happens to _____ a word, she will not win the game.

2. Betty got up to _____ the cups with milk.

3. Cheating is an _____ way to win.

4. Jon needed to _____ his dinner when it got cold.

5. I _____ my pail, but then I spotted it under my seat.

supplies	dismay	beam	recover	cure

A. Vocabulary Words: Cloze Paragraph Use the correct word from above to complete each sentence.

In the land of Flaim, the king became ill. All the **1.** _____

in the kingdom did not help. The queen was filled with **2.** _____.

She feared the king was so sick that he would not **3.** _____.

She ran across the land, trying to find a **4.** _____ for the king.

She found it, and she came home to heal the king. The king began to

5. _____. "You saved me!" he said.

B. Vocabulary Strategy:
Synonyms Use this thesaurus entry to answer the questions that follow.

1. What are the guide words on this

page? _____

2. What word means the same thing as

fragrance? _____

3. What are two other synonyms for
fragrance?

_____

fragment/frame

fragment [*n*] bit, chip, chunk, particle,
  shred, slice, sliver

fragrance [*n*] aroma, perfume, scent,
  smell

frail [*adj*] brittle, breakable, delicate,
  feeble, tender, weak

frame [*n*] body, cage, enclosure, form,
  fringe, hem, outline, trimming

© Macmillan/McGraw-Hill

Name _____

As you reread "Ray and Blaine Save the Day," fill in the Cause and
Effect Chart.

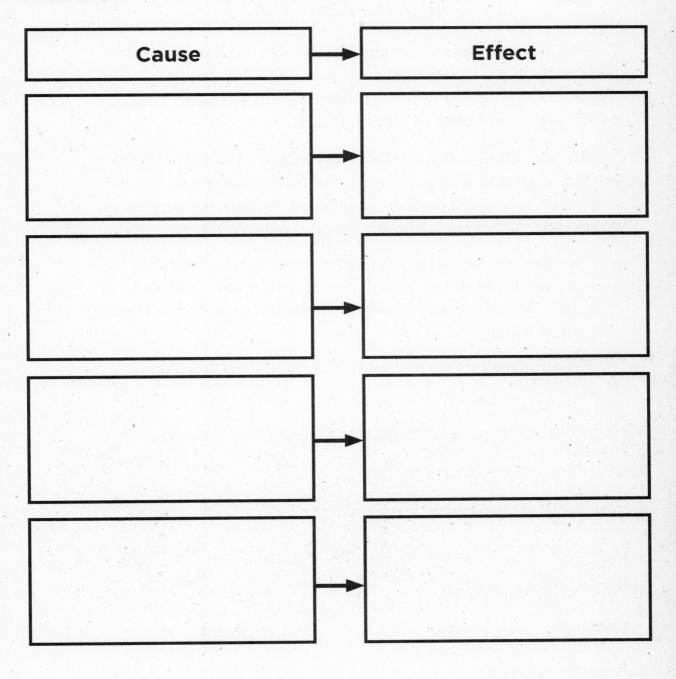

| Cause | → | Effect |

Name _____

Read the passage. Then complete the questions.

Hooray for Faith!

Mr. Stevens had lived by himself for a long time. He felt well and strong, but there were things he could not do. He could no longer see very well. Now even a bright light was just a faint gray haze. There was no cure for his failing sight.

His son, Clay, wanted his dad to stay at home. But his dad could not live unassisted. Clay got a dog named Faith. Faith was trained to help people who could not see. Clay also got his dad some supplies to help take care of Faith. The dog appealed to both of them.

One day, Mr. Stevens took a misstep. He fell down the stairs and sprained his ankle. He was filled with dismay and wailed in pain. Faith heard his plea. She hit the phone and pressed 9-1-1. Then she barked into the receiver.

Soon, people came to rescue Mr. Stevens. He was proud of Faith. She did her job well.

1. Underline words in the passage that have the long *a* sound.

2. Circle the prefixes in the passage.

3. What caused Mr. Stevens to sprain his ankle?

_____

4. Why did Faith get help?

_____

5. A call for help is a _____.

        peal   plea   play

At Home: Reread the passage and talk about dogs that help people, like Faith.

Read the passage. Then complete the questions.

Land Snakes and Water Snakes

All snakes can swim. Many spend a lot of time in the water. We tend to call these water snakes. Land snakes are those that you will find in tall grass, woods, or even in a backyard.

Water snakes cool their bodies in the water. Then they need the sun's heat. These snakes will sit on rocks or on tree branches and sun themselves.

Land snakes often have smaller heads than water snakes. They cool their bodies by hiding under logs and rocks. They warm up their bodies in the sun, as well.

1. Underline the following signal words or phrases in the passage:
all   than   as well

2. Put a box around the subjects being compared and contrasted.

3. Now write the differences and similarities between the subjects on the lines below.

_____

_____

_____

_____

Read the passage. Then complete the questions.

Rocket Engines

It is not easy to get a space shuttle off the ground! A rocket engine is a reaction engine. That means that a lot of energy pushes one way, in order to move the rocket the other way.

> This sentence tells an important detail.

Picture a man wearing roller skates. He can push off a wall and roll back to the wall. But, if he pushes very hard, he will roll quite fast. How fast he rolls is the reaction to the push he gave.

Rockets push very hot gas down in order to send the rocket and space shuttle up. As a shuttle gets higher, it does not need rockets anymore. The rockets fall away. The shuttle keeps going into space.

1. Underline one important detail in each paragraph that helps you summarize.

2. How does a rocket engine work? Put a box around the sentence that tells us.

3. Write a summary of the second paragraph on the lines.

_____

_____

_____

_____

_____

Read the passage. Then complete the questions.

Fang to the Rescue

Kit's dog Fang was trained to find people who were trapped underground. So Kit and her mom brought Fang to sites to practice looking for people. Fang had to trace a smell and find where a person was buried. Fang stayed for days practicing.

One day, a building fell. Many people got out in time. But everyone was afraid that someone might be trapped.

A team trainer put on Fang's leash and followed Fang around the site. Fang found a smell and then began to bark. Therefore, the rest of the team came in and cleared the rubble. A man was alive, but trapped.

The team got the man out. Kit was very proud of Fang!

This is a signal word.

This sentence is a cause.

1. Underline the following signal words in the passage:
   so   then   therefore

2. Put a box around the causes in the passage.

3. Now write the effect of Fang's barking on the lines.

_____

_____

_____

_____

**Draw a line under the word that best completes each sentence.
Write the word on the line.**

1. If you wish to see the sea, you go on a _____.

   shape   shop   ship

2. Large animals that swim in the sea are _____.

   whales   phones   mules

3. At the end of the day, May must _____ her ponytail.

   braided   paycheck   unbraid

4. I will leave you in the shop, but make sure you do not _____.

   backpack   misbehave   unfreeze

5. Sam cleaned the mud off her feet in the _____.

   backrub   bandstand   bathtub

6. Can Dad toss that junk in the _____ ?

   trashcan   weekend   shopping

7. When Pete kept messing up, he felt _____.

   misread   unlucky   misplaced

8. You made me get lost! You _____ me!

   misled   unfilled   sagged

© Macmillan/McGraw-Hill

Name _____

The letters *i, y,* and *igh* can all make the long *i* sound.

A. Underline the long *i* sound in the words below.

high	by	flight	grind	sly
cry	light	kind	myself	pint

B. Circle each word in the puzzle. Look for the long *i* patterns to help you.

f	l	i	g	h	t	i	g	h
g	r	i	n	d	i	l	y	p
c	g	y	k	s	n	d	n	i
r	h	y	h	i	g	h	t	n
y	t	g	n	i	n	d	f	t
k	i	m	y	s	e	l	f	y
k	i	n	d	l	i	g	h	t
f	r	i	b	y	i	g	h	y

C. Use the correct words from above to complete each sentence.

1. What ☐__ __ __ of cake do you like?

2. I can read all by __ __ __ ☐__ __.

3. Please get a __☐__ __ of ice cream.

4. The ☐__ __ __ __ went off and it was dark.

Write the letters from the boxes above to spell a secret message!

Cats __ __ __ __ to go up in trees.

     4 3 1 2

A. **As you read, pay attention to pauses, stops, and end punctuation.**

	Twyla has a tan cat named Sy. She does not like to let Sy
14	outside. But, Sy can be sneaky! He escapes out the front door. Sy
27	runs into a huge, fierce dog! Sy leaps up into a tree and sits on a
43	branch.
44	Getting up the tree is easier for Sy than getting down. Twyla
56	sets out treats, but Sy is stuck. He cannot get down. Can Twyla and
70	Brian think of a good plan to save Sy? What might you try if you
85	were Twyla? 87

B. **Read these words to yourself. Then have a partner time you. Do it two more times to see if you can beat your score!**

Twyla	right	thigh	tree	clean
sighed	by	light	rain	leaf
cried	fine	why	peel	day
fright	liked	fly	stayed	waved
Brian	high	giant	dismay	safe

Record Your Scores

Time 1: _____   Time 2: _____   Time 3: _____

At Home: Write two sentences using the words above. Then read them aloud.

© Macmillan/McGraw-Hill

Name _____

Inflectional endings are letters that you can add to the end of word to change the word's meaning. Sometimes we have to change a *y* to an *i* before adding *-es* or *-ed*.

A. **Fill in the missing parts to make the bold-faced word.**

1. The bird **flies** into the trees.

   fly − y + i + _____ = flies

2. She **copies** the sentences from the board.

   copy − y + _____ + _____ = copies

3. He **hides** behind the tree.

   _____ + _____ = hides

4. She **emptied** the bucket.

   empty − _____ + _____ = emptied

5. The boy **tried** to pull the wagon.

   _____ − _____ + _____ = tried

B. **Write two sentences about animals. Use the word *flies* in one sentence. Use the word *tried* in the other.**

1. _____

   _____

2. _____

   _____

Name _____

A. Vocabulary Words Check *true* or *false* for each statement.

1. A prisoner who escapes from his cell is badly behaved. ☐true ☐false

2. You would be **fierce** at a birthday party. ☐true ☐false

3. You are standing still when you are **trembling**. ☐true ☐false

4. If you saw a monster, you would scream in **fright**. ☐true ☐false

5. A bird can rest on its **perch**. ☐true ☐false

B. Vocabulary Strategy: Context Clues Underline the idioms in the passage.

The last leg of the trip was difficult. Our family had been on the road for many weeks. We were going west on the Oregon Trail. We saw quite a few things that caused **fright** along the way. We saw an eagle on its **perch**. Then, we saw a **fierce** bear smack in the middle of the trail. We were **trembling** as we **escaped** the bear. But now we are finally in Oregon. After all is said and done, I am glad we made the trip.

Use the correct bold-faced word from above to complete each sentence.

1. The girl was mad and had a _____ look on her face.

2. When you jumped out of the tree, it gave me quite a _____.

3. The cat watched the mouse from its _____ in the tree.

4. She was so worried before her speech, she was _____.

5. Ted _____ the house before the fire reached his room.

Name _____

After reading "The Problem with Sy," fill in the Inferences Chart to help you make inferences about the story.

Text Clues	What You Know	Inferences

Read the passage. Then complete the questions.

The Bat House

In shop class, Mr. Sung said, "We will make a bat house."

"Bats? No way!" Tyler cried. He was trembling with fright.

"Bats are not fierce. They only fly at night," explained Mr. Sung.

"That's right!" said Myra. "Bats keep pests from eating crops."

"They need a safe place to escape owls," said Mr. Sung.

The bat house was 12 feet high and three feet long. They placed it behind a stream. In a week, bats had come to stay. The kids saw the bats on their perches.

"I'm glad the bats have a home," sighed Tyler.

1. Underline the long *i* patterns in the story.

2. Circle the words that contain inflectional endings in the passage.

3. How does Tyler feel about bats at the end of the story?

   _____

4. Why do bats need a safe place to live?

   _____

5. Birds rest on a _____.
         table   perch   chair

© Macmillan/McGraw-Hill

At Home: Reread the passage and talk about your biggest fears.

Name _____

Sometimes *g*, as in *large*, is soft and it sounds like a *j*. Sometimes *c*, as in *city*, is soft and sounds like an *s*.

A. Underline the word that best completes each sentence. Write the word on the line.

1. My mother's ring has a very special _____.

get   gem   germ

2. The juice costs 95 _____.

cents   clams   crabs

3. There are lots of things to do in a big _____.

claw   city   creek

4. My favorite class at school is _____.

gym   jelly   trick

5. Where is the best _____ to go for pizza?

play   place   face

6. Did you read that _____ already?

bridge   huge   page

7. Can I borrow your _____ to do my math homework?

cinder   pencil   cycle

8. Stan likes his water cold so he adds _____.

ice   fancy   circle

B. Go back and circle the soft consonants in the answers above.

Name _____

**A. Have a partner time you as you read the passage.
Record your scores below.**

	Trees help people in many ways. They give us air to breathe.
12	We can cut trees to get wood to make fires and build things. The
26	pages in books come from trees as well.
34	But, many forests are in danger. We should be concerned!
44	Young trees are fragile, and they take time to grow back. The large
57	trees around young trees help protect them. If we cut all the trees in
71	one space, the young trees cannot thrive. We have cut back forests
83	too much recently. How can we help the trees? 92

Record Your Scores

First Read: Words Read _____   Time _____

Second Read: Words Read _____   Time _____

B. Partners Use this chart to check your partner's reading.

Speed	☐ too slow	☐ too fast	☐ just right
Paid attention to periods, commas, end punctuation	☐ never	☐ sometimes	☐ always
Accuracy	☐ skipped words	☐ self-corrected	☐ read every word
Read with feeling	☐ never	☐ sometimes	☐ always

© Macmillan/McGraw-Hill

At Home: Reread the passage and talk about how you can help save trees.

Name _____

> **Open syllables** end in a vowel and usually have a long vowel sound. **Closed syllables** end in a consonant and usually have a short vowel sound.

A. Write whether the word has open or closed syllables.

Example: limit __closed__

1. absent _____

2. dinner _____

3. future _____

4. vanish _____

5. siren _____

B. Use the correct words from above to complete each sentence.

1. I wish I could look into the _____ to know what will happen.

2. A _____ went off when smoke filled the hallway.

3. Wash your hands before you eat _____.

4. I have not been _____ from school yet.

5. If I could _____, then no one would see me.

gems	protect	ripen	disputes	concerned

A. Vocabulary Words Choose the correct word from above to complete each statement.

Example: *Neat* is to *messy* as *smooth* is to ___rumpled___ .

1. *Happy* is to *joyful* as *nervous* is to _____.

2. *Absent* is to *present* as *agrees* is to _____.

3. *Plant* is to *bloom* as *fruit* is to _____.

B. Vocabulary Strategy: Context Clues Underline the context clues that help you figure out each bold-faced word.

There was once was a very poor man. All he owned was a peach tree. He even slept under the tree. The branches were the only things that could **protect** him. The man took great care of the tree. He was always worried and **concerned** that something would happen to it. Day after day the man took care of the tree. He would watch the fruit **ripen**, or become ready to eat. One morning, to his surprise, the man woke up and all of the peaches were gone. In place of the peaches were shiny **gems**! Everyone in the town came to see. No one could **dispute** or argue the fact that they were real. The man was happy. He would never be poor again!

Use the correct bold-faced word from above to complete each sentence.

1. Her necklace is made with pretty green _____.

2. In the winter, Jack wears a jacket to _____ him from the cold.

3. My mom gets _____ if I forget to call her.

Name _____

Write the main idea of "Large Trees with Large Jobs" in the middle circle of the Main Idea Web. Then, fill in the circles around it with the details that support the main idea.

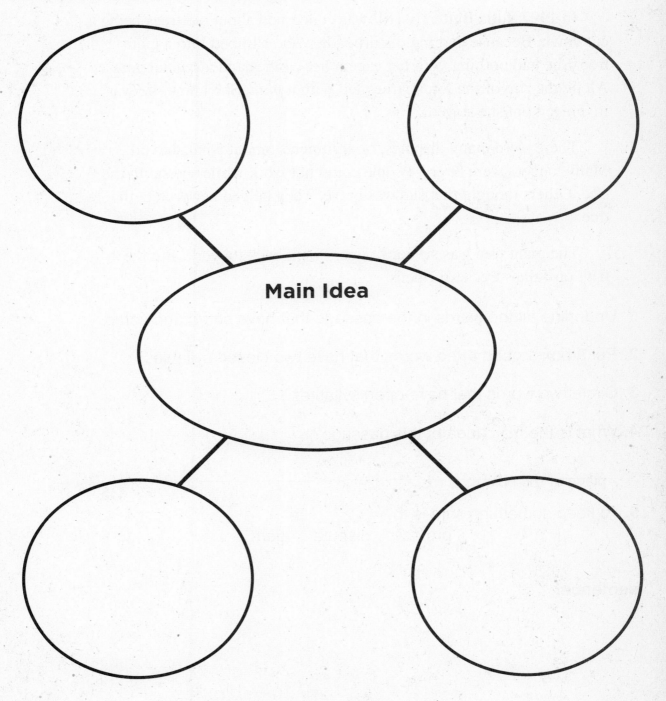

Main Idea

Name _____

Read the passage. Then complete the questions.

Julia's Tree

In 1997, Julia Butterfly Hill was concerned about old trees being cut down. Because logging disturbed her, she climbed into a giant tree. She had nothing with her except her clothes and a special gem. Along the rim of the forest, trees fell with a *thud*. She knew she was in danger, but she stayed.

There were many disputes, or arguments, about what she did. Many loggers were angry. People could not work while she sat in the tree. Others thought that she was brave. They helped her protect the tree.

The giant tree was saved! Loggers went back to work. But the fruit on Julia's tree still ripens.

1. Underline all the words in the passage that have soft *c* and soft *g*.

2. Put a box around three words that have two closed syllables.

3. Circle two words that have open syllables.

4. What is the main idea of this passage?

_____

5. To keep something safe is to _____ it.

protect   dispute   gem

© Macmillan/McGraw-Hill

Name _____

Read the passage. Then complete the questions.

Critter Care

Min wanted to start a club in her school.

You can infer from this sentence that Min wants to make friends who have the same interests.

There was already a club that played games and a club for tennis. There was a drama club and a chess club. "I want to make a new club," Min complained to her Mom. "Well, you like to help animals. Why don't you see if other kids would like to help out?"

Min thought it was a great idea. She made posters and held a meeting. Many kids showed up.

"We can spend some time at an animal shelter," said Tom.

"And we can raise money for sick dogs," said Polly.

"We can also help animals in the forest by making feeders and hanging them," said Ida.

"Let's call this club Critter Care! I think this will be a great club," said Min.

1. Underline the following items in the passage:
main character   problem   solution

2. Put a box around the sentences about which you can make inferences.

3. Now write the inferences you made on the lines.

_____

_____

_____

Name _____

Read the passage. Then complete the questions.

Hope for the Chestnut Tree

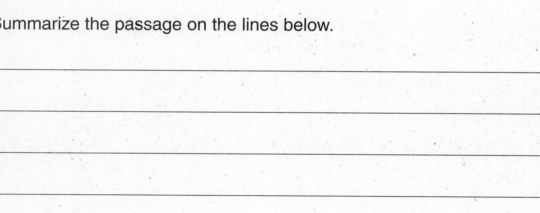

In 1902, chestnut trees were found across most of the United States. By 1926, most of the chestnut trees were dying from the chestnut blight, a fungus that gets in the trees and kills them.

What caused this tragedy? In 1876, chestnut trees from Japan carried the blight. Trees from Japan were sent all over the United States. Many chestnuts got sick in a short time.

Recently, people have been trying to save the chestnut. Scientists know what keeps the trees from Japan healthy. They are helping the trees in the United States stay healthy as well.

1. Circle the main idea of the passage.

2. Underline two details that support the main idea.

3. Summarize the passage on the lines below.

_____

_____

_____

_____

_____

Name _____

Digraphs are two or more letters that work together to make one sound. Examples are *ch* and *tch*.

A. **Underline the digraphs in the words below.**

branch	witch	check	patch	cheap
catch	chin	stretch	chop	crunch

B. **Circle each word in the puzzle. Look for the digraphs to help you.**

c	h	e	a	p	e	d	d	c
h	a	p	c	i	s	g	i	r
e	w	h	c	n	t	w	g	u
c	l	a	h	e	r	i	g	n
k	o	k	o	d	e	t	i	c
e	a	w	p	a	t	c	h	h
c	a	t	c	h	c	h	i	n
b	r	a	n	c	h	t	c	h

C. **Use the correct words from above to complete each sentence.**

1. Pat will toss the ball and Cindy will __ __ □ __ __ it.

2. I got the pants because they were __ __ □ __ __.

3. My swing hung from the __ __ □ __ __ __ of a tree.

4. When Will's pants ripped, he had to place a □ __ __ __ __ on them.

Write the letters from the boxes above to spell a secret message!

What starts with a T, ends with a T, and is full of tea?

A __ __ __ __ ot!
  1 2 3 4

Name _____

A. As you read, pay attention to speed and tempo.

	In the United States, people value the freedoms they have.
10	Some of the freedoms we have today are freedom of the press,
22	freedom of speech, and the freedom to vote. But after the
33	Revolutionary War, that gave citizens in the United States many
43	freedoms, many men and women were still enslaved.
51	For these people, freedom seemed out of reach. Life was so bad
63	that they chose to make a trip that held much danger. To escape,
76	they had to travel north. They had no chart except the stars in the
90	sky. They risked their lives each pitch-black night to gain relief.
102	Many tried, but only some succeeded. 108

B. Read these words. Then have a partner time you.
Do it two more times to see if you can beat your score!

choose	hitch	chase	gel	ace
church	chop	rich	age	try
coach	patch	teach	sight	cent
stitch	ditch	rice	huge	race
match	chin	cell	mile	rage

Record Your Scores

Time 1: _____   Time 2: _____   Time 3: _____

© Macmillan/McGraw-Hill

At Home: Write three sentences using the words above
and see how fast you can read them.

Name _____

> **Suffixes** are letters that are added to the end of a word. The suffixes -*er* and -*or* are used to tell what a person does for their work or for a hobby. An example is a *waiter*.

A. **Fill in the missing parts to make the bold-faced word.**

1. The **teacher** smiled.

   teach + _____ **= teacher**

2. We clapped as the **singer** sang a song.

   _____ **+** _____ **= singer**

3. The **sailor** sailed his ship up the coast.

   _____ **+** _____ **= sailor**

4. Mr. Chaps asked the **baker** to sell him a cake.

   _____ **–** _____ **+** _____ **=** _____

5. On my team, each of the **players** helps us win.

   _____ **+** _____ **+** _____ **=** _____

B. **Write two sentences about jobs. Use the word *teacher* in one sentence. Use the word *baker* in the other.**

1. _____

   _____

2. _____

   _____

A. Vocabulary Words Check *true* or *false* for each statement.

1. All **citizens** have rights. ☐true ☐false

2. A winner is a person who has **succeeded**. ☐true ☐false

3. Carrying a huge load will bring you **relief**. ☐true ☐false

4. A **dedicated** sports team tries very hard. ☐true ☐false

5. When you **advise** someone you do not talk to them. ☐true ☐false

B. Vocabulary Strategy: Inflectional Endings Circle the word that best completes each sentence. Write the word on the line.

1. Last week, Fred _____ up the steps two at a time.
   jumping   jumps   jumped

2. Craig feeds his three _____ each day.
   cat   cating   cats

3. Mandy is _____ in the race, and she hopes she will win.
   run   running   runned

4. If five _____ help, we can do so much!
   kid   kidding   kids

5. Why is the robin _____ so high?
   flying   fly   flies

© Macmillan/McGraw-Hill

Name _____

As you reread "Which Way to Freedom?" find two main ideas that the story discusses. Then find details that support the main ideas. Use them to fill out two Main Idea Webs.

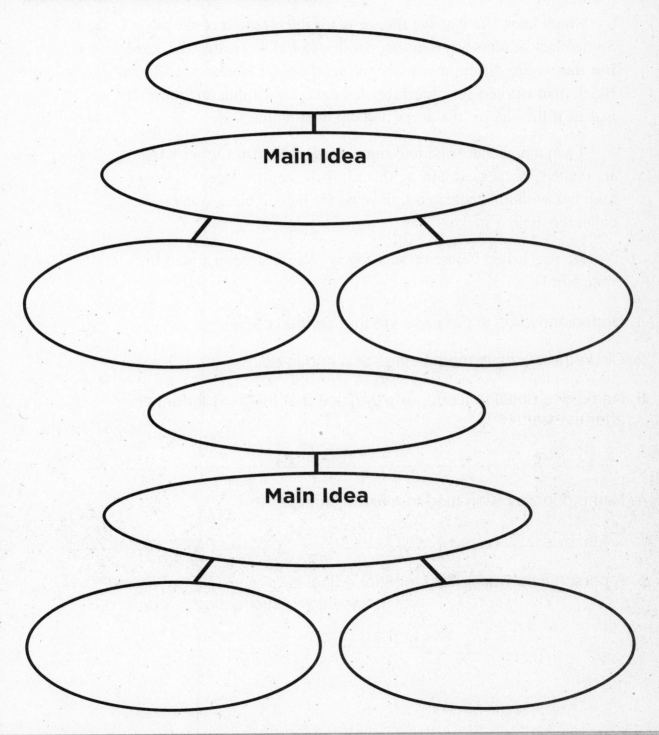

Main Idea

Main Idea

Read the passage. Then complete the questions.

Martin Luther King, Jr.

Much later, life was not the same for the children of slaves. Some black leaders advised that people should be treated the same. But there were different schools and teachers for blacks and whites. Black men worked very hard for cheap wages without any relief. It was as if the chains of slavery had not been unhitched.

Then a preacher tried making a change. Martin Luther King, Jr., made speeches explaining that all men are the same. He led marches with his dedicated followers. He helped black trash collectors hold a strike.

He was killed before he succeeded. We must never forget his wise words.

1. Underline words in the passage that contain *ch*.

2. Circle the words in the passage that end in *ed*.

3. Name one detail that supports the idea that things were unfair after the war.

_____

4. Name one way King tried to make a change.

_____

5. A person who works hard to meet a goal is _____.

   dedicated   succeeded   advised

At Home: Reread the passage and talk about why Martin Luther King, Jr. is a leader.

© Macmillan/McGraw-Hill

Name _____

A long *o* sound can be made with the letters *o* and *oa*.

A. Underline the letters that make the long o sound in the words below.

pony	toad	troll	toast	cold
sold	oak	solo	soap	coast

B. Read the clues. Then use the words to complete the sentences.

Across

1. You can see the ocean from the __.

2. Are you worried about playing __?

3. Our class has a pet __.

4. Ed has an __ tree in his yard.

5. The __ had a mean face.

Down

1. The man __ Bob three pens.

2. I wash my hands with __.

3. I eat __ for breakfast.

4. I shiver when I am __.

5. You can ride a __.

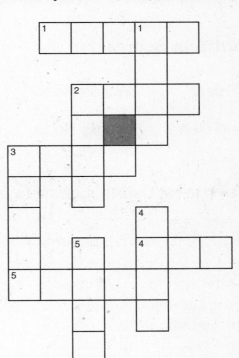

Name _____

A. Have a partner time you as you read the passage.
Record your scores below.

	Joan really loves to go to the big parade. She loves to hear the
14	banjos and steel drums play. She loves to see the floats and the
27	people dressed up in costumes. There is so much excitement!
37	She asked her dad if she could dance this year. "I'm nine years
50	old!" she cried. "I can dance!" Mr. Loman said it would be okay.
63	But he told her that she could not stop, even if she got tired. Joan is
79	ready to dance with all the folks who stroll along in the parade. 92

Record Your Scores

First Read: Words Read _____   Time _____

Second Read: Words Read _____   Time _____

B. Partners Use this chart to check your partner's reading.

Speed	☐ too slow	☐ too fast	☐ just right
Paid attention to periods, commas, end punctuation	☐ never	☐ sometimes	☐ always
Accuracy	☐ skipped words	☐ self-corrected	☐ read every word
Read with feeling	☐ never	☐ sometimes	☐ always

At Home: Reread the passage together and talk about why
Joan is so excited.

Name _____

Contractions combine two words with an apostrophe. The apostrophe usually takes the place of a vowel in the second word. Example: *hasn't = has + not*

A. **Draw a line from each pair of words to its contraction.**

could not   that's

she is   isn't

is not   couldn't

I have   I've

that is   she's

B. **Read each sentence. Write the contraction for the underlined words.**

1. She <u>is not</u> late for school.   _____

2. I <u>could not</u> find the milk.   _____

3. <u>She is</u> in the chess club.   _____

4. <u>That is</u> my house.   _____

5. <u>I have</u> got to go.   _____

A. Vocabulary Words Circle the word or phrase in the group that does not belong with the bold-faced word.

1. **excitement**   bored   happy   smile

2. **refused**   no   turned down   thank you

3. **fabric**   sewing   grape juice   clothes

4. **boasted**   bragged   proud   shy

5. **shrieked**   whispered   screamed   yelled

6. **costumes**   dress up   school clothes   play

7. Which would you rather **refuse**? Tell why on the lines below.
   a. a million dollars   **b.** a million bugs

_____

_____

B. Vocabulary Strategy: Suffixes Read each sentence and look closely at the bold-faced word. Find the meaning of this word in the phrases at the right. Draw a line from the word to its meaning.

1. That actress is **famous**.   having poison

2. The red berries are **poisonous**.   full of joy

3. She was so happy, she was **joyous**.   having great fame

As you read "Joan's First Parade," fill in the Story Map to help you find the problem and solution.

Character

Setting

Problem

Events

Solution

Name _____

Read the passage. Then complete the questions.

Logan's Trip

Logan and his mom were on a trip to Jamaica. This momentous trip was hard because Logan had been very ill. As they crossed a road, Logan boasted that he was going to swim and go on a boat!

His mom refused. "Logan, you must be cautious or you will get sick again."

Logan sighed. Suddenly, he noticed costumes made with bright fabric. He could hear steel drums and banjos approaching.

"It's a festival!" said his mother.

"Let's go!" Logan shrieked.

Huge floats rolled by with dancers and singers. Clowns roamed around and amused people. All the excitement cheered Logan up. He had fun after all!

1. Underline the words in the passage that make the long *o* sound.

2. Circle the contractions in the passage.

3. What is Logan's problem at the beginning of the passage?

_____

_____

4. What was Logan's solution?

_____

5. The clowns were wearing _____.

              costumes   boots   jeans

© Macmillan/McGraw-Hill

At Home: Reread the passage and talk about what makes parades and festivals exciting.

Name _____

> **Diphthongs** are vowel sounds made by a gliding action in the mouth. Examples include the *ou* in *house*, the *ow* in *cow*.

A. Circle the word that best completes each sentence.
Write the word on the line.

1. You can get apples and other fruit in _____.

top   town   tower

2. Fran stopped to smell the red _____.

flow   floss   flower

3. At the end of the act, Ed clapped for the _____.

clown   claw   clout

4. If you lose something, check the lost and _____.

found   pound   sound

5. Have you ever wanted to float on a _____?

proud   loud   cloud

6. We found a lot of change in the seats of the _____.

count   couch   crouch

7. If you don't learn how to swim you might _____.

crowd   crown   drown

8. Don't talk if you have a _____ full of food.

mouth   south   gown

B. Go back and underline the letters that make the *ou* sound in the answers above.

A. Use this passage to perform a choral reading or Readers Theater.

10	**Interviewer:** Good morning, Mr. Roundhouse. Can I ask a few questions?
11	**Cowboy:** Howdy! Go ahead. I know all about being a cowboy.
22	**Interviewer:** How do you round up the cows?
30 / 42	**Cowboy:** I ride around and shout. The sound of my voice tells them that they have to move.
48	**Interviewer:** What does a rodeo clown do?
55 / 67	**Cowboy:** If a rider falls, the clown swiftly distracts the bull. That way we can get the rider to safety.
75 / 86	**Interviewer:** Wow! That sounds hard. I have one last question. Do you like being in town or out on the range?
96 / 110	**Cowboy:** I don't like how loud it is in town. I'd rather be driving cows or roaming on the range. 116

B. Read these silly sentences aloud. Pause when you see (/) and stop when you see (//). Change your voice when you see a question mark (?) or an exclamation point (!).

1. Did the cow chow?// Or did he take a bow for the crowd? //

2. Do you want to borrow/ a pound/ of round mounds?//

3. Let's go out/ and talk about/ a pig's snout.//

4. Wow!// The clown/ put on powder/ in the shower/ and ate chowder!//

5. Let's count nouns/ as we bounce/ on the couch!//

© Macmillan/McGraw-Hill

At Home: Reread the passage and think of a few silly sentences on your own.

Name _____

Words that contain the suffix -*ly* usually describe something.

A. Combine the root word with the suffix –*ly* to make a word.

Example: ly _swiftly_

1. 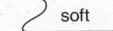 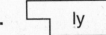 _____

2.   _____

3. ly kind _____

4.  most _____

5. 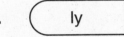 final _____

B. Use the correct words from above to complete each sentence.

1. After being awake for so long, the baby was _____ asleep.

2. The man _____ held the door open for my mother.

3. I _____ eat cake as a treat, but I will eat ice cream.

4. Shut the door _____, because the kids are all sleeping.

5. When the team lost the game, Zack was _____ upset.

Name _____

| swiftly | well-rounded | prowling | daring | roaming |

A. Vocabulary Words Choose the correct word from above to complete each statement.

Example:

Big is to *little* as *hard* is to ___soft___ .

1. *Lazy* is to *energetic* as *afraid* is to _____.

2. *Softly* is to *loudly* as *slowly* is to _____.

3. *Sprinting* is to *running* as *wandering* is to _____.

4. *Cat* is to *pouncing* as *thief* is to _____.

B. Vocabulary Strategy: Antonyms Write the letter of the antonym on the right that matches the vocabulary word on the left.

1. well-rounded ____   **a.** stay in one place

2. roaming ____   **b.** slowly

3. daring ____   **c.** dull, one-sided

4. swiftly ____   **d.** fearful

© Macmillan/McGraw-Hill

Name _____

As you reread "A Cowboy's Life," use the Inferences Chart to make inferences about cowboys. Use facts from the story and information you already know.

Text Clues	What You Know	Inferences

© Macmillan/McGraw-Hill

Read the passage. Then complete the questions.

Cowboy Tales

Cowboys are proud of their stories. At night, cowboys young and old gather around a campfire and tell their best stories. Sometimes, a well-rounded cowboy will share a poem as well.

The cowboys in their stories are usually daring and wild. They roam across the West, get into fights, and perform amazing feats. Pecos Bill is one of the most famous. Some say he was raised by prowling coyotes. People tell stories about how he swiftly rode a tornado and drained a river to water his ranch.

Rounding up cattle out on the range can get lonely. These stories give the cowboys common ground.

1. Underline words in the passage that have the *ou* sound, as in *house* and *cow*.

2. Circle the words in the passage with the suffix *-ly*.

3. What inference can you make after reading the last paragraph?

   _____

4. What are two things that a well-rounded cowboy might share around the campfire?

   _____

5. The cat _____ catches the mouse.
   swiftly   costly   falsely

At Home: Reread the passage and talk about the most interesting idea you read.

Read the passage. Then complete the questions.

Frederick Douglass

Frederick Douglass was a man who believed in freedom. He was born a slave. He could not read or write. Like all slaves, he worked hard and slept for a short time. He was often mistreated.

Frederick tricked some boys into teaching him the letters. Soon, he learned how to read. He planned escapes, and he finally succeeded. Once he was free, he told how slaves were beaten and mistreated. He explained that all men should be respected.

Frederick gave speeches during the Civil War. By 1865, all enslaved men were freed. After the war, Frederick continued to work for the rights of black people and women.

This sentence is a supporting detail.

1. Underline the main idea of the passage.

2. Put a box around another detail that supports the main idea.

3. Now write a summary of the passage on the lines below.

_____

_____

_____

_____

_____

Read the passage. Then complete the questions.

Planning a Feast

Maggie and her mama planned a big feast, but it was getting late and they needed to get ready quickly. Maggie and her mama couldn't prepare everything in time. So, everyone in the family pitched in. Maggie scrubbed potatoes and her mama cut them to roast. Then Maggie's dad broke two coconuts open. Maggie scraped the coconut meat from the shell.

Maggie's sister, Lola, made *roti*, bread with chickpeas. She beat the dough and baked it. Maggie used the coconut to make *chutney*, a kind of dipping sauce.

Then, Maggie peeled mangoes. She couldn't take out the pits, so her mama cut them out.

This sentence shows another problem that Maggie has. What is the solution?

Finally, Maggie's family and friends came to the feast. There was so much food that everyone was full. Maggie was so proud!

1. Underline the problem in the story.

2. Put a box around the solution.

3. What was the solution to Maggie's problem with the mangoes?

_____

_____

_____

_____

Name _____

Read the passage. Then complete the questions.

The Rodeo: A Dangerous Life

Trick riding is a dangerous part of a rodeo. Riders purposely slip off the saddle of a galloping horse. Any rider can fall and be trampled.

Another part is riding a bull. The crowd watches as a rider hangs on to a wildly kicking bull. Riders fall sometimes. Rodeo clowns distract the bull while others get the rider out of the way.

> This sentence is a clue that can help you make an inference.

Roping is another part of rodeo. The roper swiftly tosses a lasso around an animal, like a cow or sheep, and ties it up.

1. Write a sentence or two about something you already knew about cowboys or trick riding before you read the passage.

   _____

2. Now make inferences about what you think the author wants you to know.

   _____

   _____

   _____

   _____

3. Underline the story clues that led you to your inference.

Name _____

**Draw a line under the word that best completes each sentence.
Write the word on the line.**

1. We _____ eaten all day.
   hasn't   haven't   have't

2. Jeff placed first in the race, so he is the _____.
   winner   wound   minnow

3. The man _____ held the door open for my mom.
   kindly   mostly   rudely

4. When Fred's bag is too heavy, his mom _____ it for him.
   candies   carries   cares

5. When we leave the house for a bit we put our puppy in the _____.
   pager   fudge   cage

6. The doctor advised the child not to _____ his bug bites.
   match   scratch   attach

7. We walked along the _____ and let the water touch our toes.
   coast   roast   most

8. I tried to read ten _____ before I went to sleep.
   pages   bowl   wage

Name _____

> The letters *oo* sometimes make the same sound as the *u* in *flute*.

**A. Circle the word that best completes each sentence.
Write the word on the line.**

1. Dad is not home now, but he will be back _____.

son   soon   soot

2. Fran zips up her coat when she gets _____.

cool   clue   tool

3. Ed jumped when the owl made a _____ sound.

fool   hoot   toe

4. Kate was hungry, so she went to get some _____.

foot   hood   food

5. Don't leave! I want to go, _____!

two   toot   too

6. _____ was closed today because of the bad weather.

moose   school   proof

7. After she brushes the dog's fur it feels _____.

smooth   shampoo   tooth

8. He used a _____ to mix the chocolate in the milk.

book   look   spoon

**B. Go back and underline the *oo* pattern that sounds like the
u in *flute*, above.**

Name _____

A. As you read, pay attention to pauses, stops, and end punctuation.

	My friends and I were patriots. We believed that our new country
12	should be free of the King's rules. We did not like the tax on tea. We
28	also did not like the Stamp Act, which put a tax on paper.
41	One cool December night, we painted our faces to fool the
52	British troops. We sneaked onto a ship that carried chests of tea. We
65	worked fast in the moonlight, chopping open the chests and pitching
76	them into the water.
80	The next day, the water was as dark as tea! They called what we
94	did a "tea party"! The British troops were in a bad mood. We showed
108	them we didn't like their rules. 114

B. Read these words to yourself. Then have your partner time you. Do it two more times to see if you can beat your score!

tooth	stool	food	cow	loud
balloon	zoom	boot	sound	room
boom	moon	food	roof	pool
soon	fool	too	out	bow
tool	root	raccoon	pout	owl

Record Your Scores

Time 1: _____   Time 2: _____   Time 3: _____

At Home: Write a paragraph using five of the words above and read it aloud.

Name _____

Look for smaller words in a big word to figure out how to pronounce the big word. Sometimes finding the smaller word will even help you figure out the meaning of the bigger word.

A. Which word is a compound? Show the two words within the compound word.

Example: **sunshine**   **wedding**   ___sun shine___

1. complicate   seashell   _____

2. lunchbox   dolphin   _____

3. windmill   unwillingly   _____

4. activity   clubhouse   _____

5. candle   outside   _____

B. Use the correct words from above to complete each sentence.

6. Matt watched the huge _____ spin.

7. It was raining, so Cass could not go _____.

8. When I place a _____ on my ear, I hear the sound of waves.

9. Andy and his friends made a _____ so that they could meet.

10. Cathy put a sandwich, a peach, and a drink in her _____.

| country | idea | sign | swooped | patriots |

A. Vocabulary Words Check *yes* or *no* for each question.

1. Is Mexico a **country**? ☐ yes ☐ no

2. Can you bake an **idea** on the stove? ☐ yes ☐ no

3. Can a lot of clapping be a **sign** that you did a nice job? ☐ yes ☐ no

4. If a robin **swooped** onto its perch, did it jump up? ☐ yes ☐ no

5. Did **patriots** fight for freedom? ☐ yes ☐ no

B. Vocabulary Strategy: Word Families Write the letter of the word on the right that is in the same word family as the word on the left.

1. run ____   **a.** countries

2. unkind ____   **b.** runner

3. breathe ____   **c.** furry

4. fur ____   **d.** breathing

5. country ____   **e.** kindly

Name _____

As you reread "A Ride in the Moonlight," fill in the Conclusions Chart.

Text Clues	Conclusion

Read the passage. Then complete the questions.

Saving Paul Revere

John Lewis was a boatman and a patriot. On April 18 at about ten o'clock, he waited near a boat with his girlfriend, Sara Moody. Soon, Paul Revere swooped by and whispered, "They are coming by sea. We must cross now!"

Lewis squinted to see the signal. It was true! Two lanterns hung in the tower of Old North Church! "Dear sir," he said. "We cannot move. The oars will make too much noise. If the British hear us, it will be our doom."

"We must quiet the oars with something," said Revere.

"I have an idea! Take this blanket to soothe the sound," said Sara. She helped Revere and Lewis loop strips of the blanket around the oars.

"John, dear, send me a sign to tell me you are well," pleaded Sara. He nodded. The moonlight shone brightly as they scooted across the Charles River to save their country.

1. Underline words in the passage that have the variant vowel *oo*.

2. Circle the compound words in the passage.

3. What was the sign that told Paul that the British were coming by sea?

_____

4. How does Sara Moody feel at the end of the story?

_____

5. A person who fights for freedom is a _____.

    sniper   citizen   patriot

At Home: Reread the passage and talk about the most surprising thing you read.

© Macmillan/McGraw-Hill

When the letter *r* follows a vowel, the sound of that vowel changes. Examples are *car* and *hard*.

A. Draw a line under the word that best completes each sentence. Write the word on the line.

1. I didn't finish my painting yet, and Hope didn't even _____ hers.

stack   start   star

2. Dad put five different fruits in the shopping _____.

cart   car   chart

3. Art fell off a swing and broke his _____.

book   harm   arm

4. You paint so well! You should be an _____!

armchair   artwork   artist

5. Patrick gazed up at the _____ in the night sky.

sharks   spars   stars

6. My nana spent two hours in the _____.

garden   cart   dart

7. Sarah made a _____ to go with her new coat.

scarf   tar   tart

8. I have a nightlight because I don't like to sleep in the _____.

spark   dark   jar

B. Go back and circle the *ar* pattern in the answer choices above.

Name _____

A. Have a partner time you as you read the passage. Record your scores below.

	Many years ago, women like Susan B. Anthony did not have the
12	same rights as men. Even if a woman worked on a farm her whole
26	life, cleaning the barn and harvesting the crops, she could never own
38	it. It belonged to her husband! This did not make any sense.
50	Susan B. Anthony was a smart lady who started a change. She
62	decided that women should take part in the voting process. She took
74	charge of a committee that worked to change the laws and grant
86	women the right to vote. "Why aren't women and enslaved people
97	treated equally?" she asked. The laws of the country did not seem
109	fair, and Susan B. Anthony was set on changing things. 119

Record Your Scores

First Read: Words Read _____   Time _____

Second Read: Words Read _____   Time _____

B. Partners Use this chart to check your partner's reading.

Speed	☐ too slow	☐ too fast	☐ just right
Paid attention to periods, commas, end punctuation	☐ never	☐ sometimes	☐ always
Accuracy	☐ skipped words	☐ self-corrected	☐ read every word
Read with feeling	☐ never	☐ sometimes	☐ always

© Macmillan/McGraw-Hill

At Home: Reread the passage and talk about what you know about Susan B. Anthony.

Name _____

> The suffix -er can mean *more than*. The suffix -est means *most*.
> They both can be used to compare things.

A. Draw a line to connect the word with its comparatives.

1. tall   shorter   thinnest

2. short   taller   shortest

3. wild   thinner   tallest

4. cold   colder   wildest

5. thin   wilder   coldest

**B. Read each sentence. Circle the correct comparative to replace
the underlined word.**

1. That was the wild ride ever!	wilder	wildest
2. Jill's hands were cold than mine.	colder	coldest
3. This is the late in music players.	later	latest
4. Eli is the fast runner on the whole team.	faster	fastest
5. I think that puppy is cute than this one.	cuter	cutest

| grant | delay | basis | committee | offended | regarding |

A. Vocabulary Words: Cloze Sentences Use the correct word from above to correctly complete each sentence.

1. I think that we should make a _____ to decide on a plan.

2. What are your feelings _____ the class play?

3. _____ us rights!" they shouted.

4. Your safety is the _____ for these rules.

5. Marty was _____ when Bart ignored him.

6. "Go as fast as you can! Do not _____!" Dad yelled.

B. Vocabulary Strategy: Dictionary Use these dictionary entries to answer the questions that follow.

1. What is the difference between the *a* in *gravity* and the *a* in *gravy*?

   _____

   _____

gravity/gravy

gravity (grav' i tē), **1.** the force that
   pulls objects to the center of Earth
gravy (grā' vē), **1.** the fat and liquid
   that comes from cooked meat

2. Which letter has a long vowel sound in both words? What sound does it have?

   _____

Name _____

As you reread "Susan B. Anthony: Making Her Mark on the Women's Rights Movement," use the Fact and Opinion Chart to identify facts and opinions.

Fact	Opinion

Read the passage. Then complete the questions.

Ida Harper

Ida Harper was the smartest partner on Susan B. Anthony's committee. She did her part by writing stories regarding women's rights. Her writing was sharper , or better, than many other writers. So Susan asked her to write *The Life and Work of Susan B. Anthony.*

Ida's hard work offended her husband. It was the basis of their divorce in 1890. But Ida did not delay. She kept writing even though her heart must have been broken.

Later, Ida worked with Carrie Catt. Carrie argued for the 19th Amendment, which granted women the right to vote. Ida wrote more books and did not stop working for women's rights.

1. Underline words in the passage that contain the *ar* sound.

2. Circle the words in the passage that use the suffixes *-er* and *-est.*

3. Is the first sentence of the passage a fact or an opinion?

_____

4. Is the last sentence of the passage a fact or an opinion?

_____

5. Jack's feelings are hurt. He is _____.

           regarded   granted   offended

© Macmillan/McGraw-Hill

At Home: Reread the passage and talk about something you learned from it.

Read the passage. Then complete the questions.

The Knitting Circle

Hannah Cooper sat by the fireplace, knitting a pair of wool socks. This pair was almost finished. The troops needed wool socks for the long winter. Last summer, the patriots had demanded freedom from British rule. Hannah's mother and father were patriots, so <u>they decided that they would not buy anything from England</u>.

This sentence has a text clue.

Hannah's mother helped the women of Newport make their own clothes. She read in the newspaper that women in Boston formed knitting circles. Now each Friday evening, women and girls came to Hannah's house to knit and sew. Here they made clothes for the troops fighting the British.

Hannah had learned to make clothes when she was five years old. She had always liked knitting. But now her knitting would help her country become free!

1. Underline text clues that let you know that Hannah's parents supported the actions of the patriots.

2. Put a box around details that help you conclude that it is cold.

3. What conclusion can you draw from the following text clue: *Hannah's mother read about knitting circles in a newspaper?* Write your answer on the lines.

_____

_____

Read the passage. Then complete the questions.

Voting for All

The Bill of Rights did not give all men the right to vote. Each state could decide which men voted and which men didn't. In 1869, the 15th amendment granted African-American men the important right to vote.

However, in 1869, many states passed laws that made it hard for African-Americans to vote. Some states kept polling places secret. States even passed unfair laws to keep African-Americans from voting!

Today all men and women in the United States can vote. Polling places are easy to find and voting is simple now. Voting is much better than it was long ago.

1. Underline three facts in the passage

2. Put a box around two opinions in the passage.

3. Now write your own opinion about voting on the lines below.

_____

_____

_____

_____

Name _____

When a vowel is followed by an *r*, such as in *bore* and *fork*, the vowel sound changes. This is an **r-controlled vowel**.

A. Circle the word that best completes each sentence. Write the word on the line.

1. What was your _____ on the test?
   score   more   pour

2. How many pals did Lee invite to the _____?
   before   horn   party

3. Do not forget to send Jay a birthday _____.
   care   card   born

4. Sal earns money by doing his _____.
   games   chores   sparks

5. When I tell my dog to speak, she _____.
   marches   barks   forks

6. Each _____ before school, I eat toast with jam.
   morning   bore   born

7. My brother _____ so loudly that I can't sleep near him!
   sport   fort   snores

8. We sat on the _____ until the rain clouds moved closer.
   storm   porch   more

B. Go back and underline the *r*-controlled vowels in the answer choices above.

© Macmillan/McGraw-Hill

A. As you read, pay attention to speed and tempo.

	It can be fun to camp in a forest. You won't be bored. There is
15	plenty to see. You might find birds, foxes, deer, or even a porcupine!
28	We are fortunate to have such beautiful forests to visit.
38	Forests are good places to visit. But not long ago, the forests
50	were in danger. People were cutting down too many trees. The land
62	was exposed. Trees were used up.
68	More and more people complained about the forests being cut
78	down. Some formal laws were made to preserve the land. It was
90	important that people forced the government to help, or else there
101	would be no trees left today! 107

B. Read these words to yourself. Then have your partner time you. Do it two more times to see if you can beat your score!

store	tore	sort	car	soon
coral	cork	port	cool	jar
chore	pork	horn	spar	loose
acorn	form	born	boot	dark
north	corn	more	char	room

Record Your Scores

Time 1: _____   Time 2: _____   Time 3: _____

© Macmillan/McGraw-Hill

At Home: Reread the passage and make up two sentences using the words above. Then, read them aloud.

Name _____

> **Prefixes** are letters that appear before a word, such as *unreal*.
> **Suffixes** are letters that appear after a word, such as *actor*.

A. **Fill in the missing parts to make the bold faced word.**

1. **Reread** the book.

   re + _____ = **reread**

2. Tory was **unable** to help me.

   _____ + _____ = **unable**

3. Don't **mistreat** your sister.

   _____ + _____ = **mistreat**

4. I was **brightly** dressed for our school pictures.

   _____ + _____ = _____

5. My grandfather was a **painter**.

   _____ + _____ = _____

B. **Write two sentences about camping. Use the word *unable* in one sentence. Use the word *mistreat* in the other.**

1. _____

   _____

2. _____

   _____

Name _____

| lantern | fortunately | declared | exposed | fragile |

A. Vocabulary Words Check *yes* or *no* for each question.

1. If you need a **lantern**, is it dark? ☐ yes ☐ no

2. If the teacher **declared** that you did well on the test, would you be happy?
☐ yes ☐ no

3. If someone is **exposed**, are they hidden? ☐ yes ☐ no

4. Would you say, "**Fortunately**, I got lost today"? ☐ yes ☐ no

5. Is a hammer **fragile**? ☐ yes ☐ no

B. Vocabulary Strategy: Prefixes Write the letter of the meaning on the right that matches the word on the left.

1. replace ____   **a.** to cook again

2. unsafe ____   **b.** different

3. misfile ____   **c.** to put back

4. recook ____   **d.** to file incorrectly

5. unlike ____   **e.** not safe

Name _____

As you reread "A Place for Us to Breathe," use the Fact and Opinion Chart to identify facts and opinions.

Fact	Opinion

Read the passage. Then complete the questions.

Insects in the Forest

In a forest, you might see the cute chipmunks, rabbits, and deer. Using your lantern, you might spy a bat or owl. But you might not notice all sorts of insects that make trees their home. Though they are small and fragile, these ordinary bugs help to break down fallen leaves.

Clearing trees sadly hurts the whole forest. Some insects cannot safely live on exposed land. Fortunately, some insects have been declared endangered. Now we must protect these little forms of life from harm and ask that loggers cut back. It is important that we care for all animals. It is unfair to ignore some animals and save others.

1. Underline words with the *or* and *ore* patterns.

2. Circle the words in the passage with prefixes and suffixes.

3. Is the last sentence in the passage a fact or opinion?

_____

4. Is the following sentence a fact or an opinion?
Some insects make trees their home.

_____

5. A glass bowl is _____.
         harsh   fragile   lantern

© Macmillan/McGraw-Hill

At Home: Reread the passage and talk about what you can do to protect animals and bugs.

When an *r* is used after a vowel, as in *blur* or *sir*, it changes the sound that the vowel makes.

A. Underline the *ir*, *er*, and *ur* patterns in the words below.

perfect   third   mermaid   curl   bird

nurse   skirt   burn   thirsty   hamburger

B. Read the clues. Then use the words to complete the sentences.

Across

1. Jen put on a shirt and a __.

2. I heard the chirp of a __.

3. If I had fins and a tail, I would be like a __.

4. Fred flipped the pancake so it would not __.

5. It wasn't too hot or too cold. It was __!

Down

1. Am I first, second, or __?

2. A pig's tail has a __.

3. Do you want to eat a __?

4. I drink milk when I am __.

5. The __ had to take my blood.

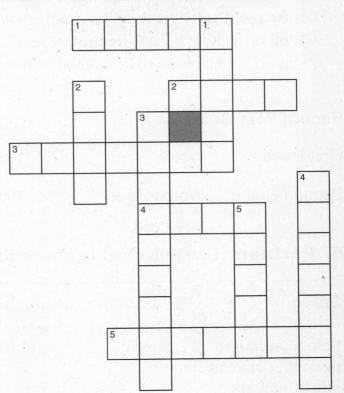

Name _____

**A. Have a partner time you as you read the passage.
Record your scores below.**

	Kurt is visiting his friend Asher for the first time. He is very
13	worried about being in the burning hot desert. It's good that there is
26	a pool near Asher's home!
31	When Kurt arrived, he saw beautiful rocks. He went to Asher's
42	house. He sat with Asher and Asher's sister, Fern, and looked at
54	many remarkable cards.
57	One card he liked had a flower on it. The flower was unique
70	because it was able to survive in the hot sand. Another had a strange
84	doll on it. Kurt became interested in the people who live in the
97	desert. What else will he find out? 104

Record Your Scores

First Read: Words Read _____   Time _____

Second Read: Words Read _____   Time _____

B. Partners Use this chart to check your partner's reading.

Speed	☐ too slow	☐ too fast	☐ just right
Paid attention to periods, commas, end punctuation	☐ never	☐ sometimes	☐ always
Accuracy	☐ skipped words	☐ self-corrected	☐ read every word
Read with feeling	☐ never	☐ sometimes	☐ always

© Macmillan/McGraw-Hill

At Home: Reread the passage and talk about a place you were nervous to go to.

The suffix -able is used to tell that an action can be done. Examples are *movable* and *drinkable*.

A. Fit the two word parts together to form a word.

Example:

son   per   __person__

1. able   drink   _____

2. able   enjoy   _____

3. able   like   _____

4. wash   able   _____

5. able   stretch   _____

B. Fill in the blanks with the word from above that makes sense.

6. Music can be very relaxing and _____ to listen to.

7. This shirt is _____ so it will fit you when you get bigger, too!

8. James is friends with the whole class, because he is very _____.

9. The milk sat out so long that it was no longer _____.

10. My shirt does not have to go to the cleaners because it is _____.

Name _____

| fret | remarkable | unique | images | echoes |

A. Vocabulary Words: Cloze Sentences Use the correct word from above to correctly complete each sentence.

1. I'm sure everything will turn out fine, so there is no need to _____.

2. When you speak while standing in the Grand Canyon, you can hear the _____ of your own voice.

3. Melissa's _____ painting was unlike her classmates' paintings.

4. The teacher told the students that they had done a _____ job.

5. The children looked at their _____ reflected in the pond.

B. Vocabulary Strategy: Thesaurus Use this thesaurus entry to answer the questions that follow.

1. What part of speech is the word *lighthearted*?

_____

lighthearted

lighthearted [adj] cheerful; free from trouble, worry, or care

SYN carefree, cheery, fun-loving, silly

ANT serious, gloomy

2. Write two synonyms for *lighthearted* that have a positive connotation.

_____

_____

3. Write the antonym for *lighthearted* that has a negative connotation.

_____

© Macmillan/McGraw-Hill

Name _____

As you reread "A Desert Vacation," use the Venn Diagram to compare
Kurt's home to Asher's.

Different

Alike

Kurt's Home   Asher's Home

Name _____

Read the passage. Then complete the questions.

Kimberly's New Home

Kimberly and her mother moved to Santa Fe. She lived in a cold place in Canada before. It snowed for nine months each year! It was great!

Her mom is a remarkable artist. Kimberly sees many unique images of purple mountains, brown deserts, and interesting birds. Kimberly thinks it is impossible to have snow in the desert.

"Don't fret," says her mom. "It will snow here, too!" Kimberly is surprised.

Kimberly likes to hear the amazing echoes when they are near the canyons. She whispers a word to see whether it will make a sound. Kimberly joins the track team just like at her old school. She is starting to get comfortable in Santa Fe.

1. Underline words in the passage that have the *er* sound.

2. Circle the words in the passage that end with the suffix *-able*.

3. What is one way Canada is different from Santa Fe?

_____

_____

4. What does Kimberly do to try to make Santa Fe feel more like her old home in Canada?

_____

_____

5. If an object is one-of-a-kind, it is _____.

echo   fret   unique

© Macmillan/McGraw-Hill

At Home: Reread the passage and talk about how Kimberly felt at different points during the story.

Name _____

When certain consonants are paired, one of them is silent.
Examples are in words such as *know, write*, and *lamb*.

A. Underline the silent consonants in the words below.

| write | knife | thumb | knew | comb |
| lamb | wrong | climb | knee | knock |

B. Circle each word in the puzzle.

l	a	m	b	w	r	o	n	g
x	a	c	r	a	c	r	d	t
k	l	o	w	k	l	j	k	h
n	s	m	r	s	i	a	n	u
i	t	b	i	p	m	x	o	m
f	v	w	t	k	b	d	c	b
e	n	b	e	n	j	t	k	n
k	n	e	w	i	k	n	e	e

C. Use the correct words from above to complete each sentence.

1. __|__|__ __ __ that down.

2. Cut the meat with a|__|__ __ __ __.

3. I can|__|__ __ __ __ up the hill.

4. If you take a __ __|__|__ __ turn you might get lost.

Write the letters from the boxes above to spell a secret message!

Did you know that basalt is the most common __ __ __ __ on Earth?
 1 4 3 2

Name _____

A. **Use this passage for a choral reading or Readers Theater.**

Directions for using your *Space Knight Jet Pack*!

8 23	*Your jet pack comes in a variety of sizes. Make sure you have the right one for you!*
26 43	**Step 1:** Untie the knot on the wrapper. You can use a knife to cut it if it will not loosen.
47	**Step 2:** Use your thumb to open TAB A. There will be a slight pop.
62	**Step 3:** Kneel to lift the jet pack onto your back.
73 85	**Step 4:** Straps should fit around your limbs snugly. Seize the straps and tighten them.
88 101	**Step 5:** Loosen the knob with your wrist. This mixes the gases and helps the jet pack work.
106 121	**Step 6:** Climb up the Safe-T-Girl Platform or on a grassy knoll. Bend your knees slightly.
124 139	**Step 7:** Press the red button. In ten seconds, the jet pack will start and you will blast off! 143

B. **Read these silly sentences aloud. Pause when you see (/) and stop when you see (//). Change your voice when you see a question mark (?) or an exclamation point (!).**

1. Did you know/ that if it snows/ my thumb goes numb?//

2. We like to walk/ and talk/ as often as we can.//

3. Put the balm/ on your palm/ and try to stay calm.//

4. The crumb/ was stuck on my thumb.// Now,/ isn't that fun?//

5. Wow!// I have a knack/ for rhyming!// Who knew?//

© Macmillan/McGraw-Hill

At Home: Reread the silly sentences above and come up with a few of your own.

Name _____

When a word ends in *-el*, *-en*, or *-le*, the last syllable is unstressed, or not as noticeable when spoken.

A. Fill in the missing parts to make the bold-faced word. Sound out the syllables.

1. The letter was **written**.

 writ + _____ = **written**

2. They drove through the **tunnel**.

 tun + _____ = **tunnel**

3. He scraped his **knuckle**.

 knuck + _____ = **knuckle**

4. She kept a **chicken** as a pet.

 _____ + _____ = _____

5. Do you have a favorite **uncle**?

 _____ + _____ = _____

B. Write two sentences about hiking. Use the word *tunnel* in one sentence. Use the word *uncle* in the other.

1. _____

 _____

2. _____

 _____

Name _____

| combing | knoll | variety | wreck | seized | grave |

A. Vocabulary Words Choose the correct word from above to complete each statement.

Example:

Neat is to *messy* as *smooth* is to __rumpled__ .

1. *Car* is to *crash* as *ship* is to _____.

2. *Teasing* is to *joking* as *searching* is to _____.

3. *Ocean* is to *desert* as *valley* is to _____.

4. *Smooth* is to *rough* as *sameness* is to _____.

5. *Won* is to *lost* as *let go* is to _____.

6. *Speedy* is to *slow* as *cheery* is to _____.

B. Vocabulary Strategy: Synonyms Write the letter of the word on the right that matches the meaning on the left.

1. fold ____   **a.** knock

2. rap ____   **b.** climb

3. branch ____   **c.** limb

4. mount ____   **d.** wrinkle

5. tiny ____   **e.** little

Name _____

Use the Conclusions Diagram to gather evidence from "Hope's
Trip to Planet Wren." Then make inferences about the story.

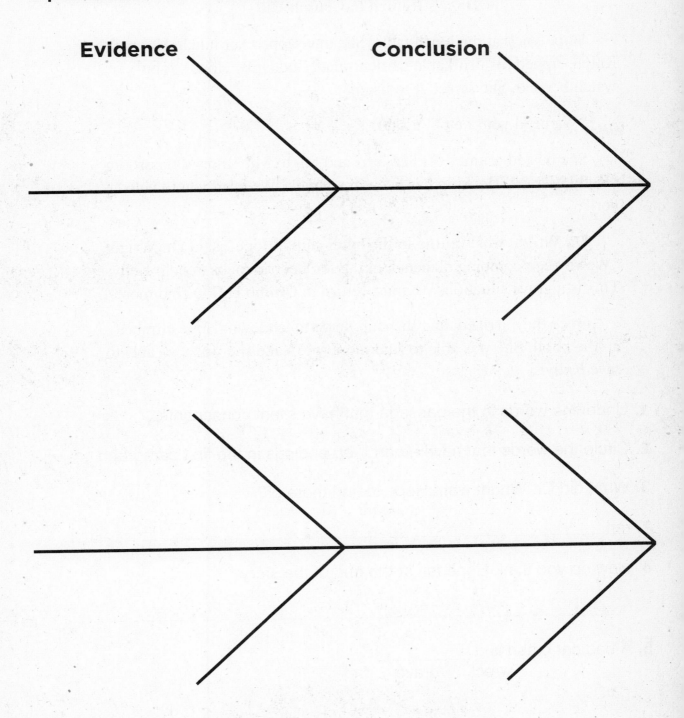

Evidence

Conclusion

Name _____

Read the passage. Then complete the questions.

Hope's Return to Crumb Hill

Hope knelt at the lunch table. She unwrapped her lunch. Her pal, Ralph, sipped his drinkable garden salad. Suddenly, Hope's robo-watch beeped. She seized it to listen.

"We need your help!" it said.

She dusted crumbs off her skirt and ran to Mr. Knorr's classroom. "Kelly is stuck. Her ship has been in a wreck! We need you to help her!"

Dr. Wright was waiting in the other ship. "Hope," said Dr. Wright. "We've been combing planets looking for electric rocks to help Kelly. This is a grave situation. We must return to Crumb Hill to find more!"

Once they arrived, and the ship made touchdown, Hope climbed up the knoll. She was able to find more rocks and she was also able to save Kelly!

1. Underline words in the passage that have silent consonants.

2. Circle the words that have -*le* and -*en* endings in the first paragraph.

3. What did Dr. Wright want Hope to find more of?

_____

4. How do you think Hope felt at the end of the story?

_____

5. A bad car crash is a _____.

       wreck   grave   fret

© Macmillan/McGraw-Hill

At Home: Reread the passage. Talk about what could happen after the story.

Name _____

Read the passage. Then complete the questions.

A Better Way to Debug

Some people reach for insect spray to get rid of garden pests. A better idea is to reach for a ladybug. Insects love to munch on garden plants, and ladybugs munch on insects. Spiders prey on many harmful insects as well.

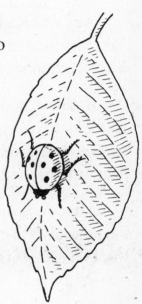

You can also spray soapy water on leaves. Insects will leave soapy leaves alone. Soap is not as harmful as insect spray. It smells better, as well!

Animals might be munching on your fresh garden vegetables. Fences keep out rabbits and deer. You can sprinkle red pepper flakes over your plants to keep cats away. These are all better ways than killing the poor insects and animals.

1. Underline the sentences that show the author's opinion.

2. Write down two facts from this passage.

_____

_____

3. After reading the passage, how do you think the author feels about insect spray?

_____

_____

Read the passage. Then complete the questions.

A Desert Family

Aza and Kareem live in a Berber village in the Sahara. Their house and school have no windows. When they wake, it is too cold to stay inside. They go into the warm sunlight.

> This is one way that Aza and Kareem are the same.

Before school Aza must gather dates from the palm trees. Kareem drives camels and gets water for their family. Their mother carries their brother Tarek on her back. That is how Kareem and Aza were carried as babies.

After Aza and Kareem go to school, Kareem farms and tends the animals. He cuts wool from the sheep for Aza. Aza dyes the wool that Kareem brings her. Then she sits with her mother and weaves a rug.

1. Underline the parts of the passage that discuss how Aza and Kareem's lives are *the same*.

2. Put a box around the parts of the passage that discuss how Aza and Kareem's lives are *different*.

3. Now write three ways that your life is different than Aza's life on the lines.

_____

_____

_____

_____

© Macmillan/McGraw-Hill

Read the passage. Then complete the questions.

Jack's First Flight

Jack Wrigley was ready to fly! He had practiced with a teacher on the Space Zoom 400 that everyone got at school. Kids had to wait until their eleventh birthdays to fly the little planes by themselves. Everyone in his class was already flying alone. He couldn't wait!

So, Jack went outside. He climbed into the light plane. It was hard for him to latch the straps on his helmet. Jack flipped the switch and then he zoomed away!

At first, it was hard to control the plane. He bounced over space rocks and tried to stay close to home. After flying a bit, he zoomed back down.

This is a signal phrase.

"What a ride!" he yelled.

1. Circle the following signal phrases in the passage:
   so   and then   at first

2. Write about what you are able to conclude from using the signal phrases.

   _____

   _____

3. Write the conclusion you can draw about what happens at the end of the passage.

   _____

   _____

A. **Combine the word parts to make a word.**

Example:

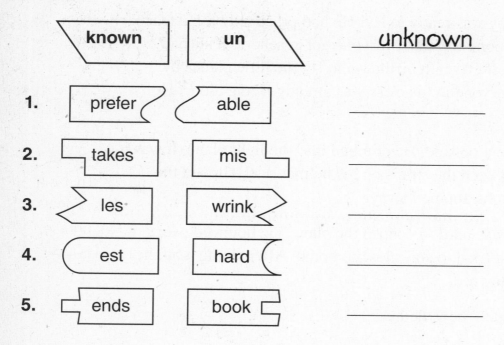

known   un   <u>unknown</u>

1. prefer   able   _____

2. takes   mis   _____

3. les   wrink   _____

4. est   hard   _____

5. ends   book   _____

B. **Fill in the blanks with the word from above that makes sense.**

1. Placing _____ on a shelf can stop books from falling over.

2. Can you flatten out the _____ on your blanket?

3. My clay pot had a few _____, but I still liked it.

4. It is _____ to use black pen when filling out forms.

5. Mark has a harder time with math than English, but art is the

_____ subject for him.

Name _____

> When the letter *i* or *y* is placed after *o*, the *o* sound changes.
> Examples are *oil* and *boy.*

A. Draw a line under the word that best completes the sentence. Write the word on the line.

1. Let the water _____ before adding the noodles.
   boil   foil   fool

2. The towel did not dry all the way, so it was still _____.
   avoid   moist   moss

3. When Dan hit his first home run, he felt a rush of _____.
   joy   toy   jay

4. The small pink doll was Ann's favorite _____.
   boy   toy   voice

5. "Come and _____ the game," Sally said to Tom.
   join   point   note

6. The crowd at the concert made a lot of _____.
   foil   noise   fold

7. Joe _____ at the dog he wanted to bring home.
   voided   painted   pointed

8. If divers aren't careful they can _____ the coral reef.
   enjoy   coil   destroy

B. Now, circle the *oi* and *oy* patterns in the answer choices above.

Name _____

A. **As you read, pay attention to end punctuation, intonation, pauses, and stops.**

	Grandpop and Roy walked into town to vote today.
9	Grandpop was in a hurry, but he said, "Roy, I'm enjoying
20	myself!" He was joyful that he could vote for a variety of
32	government offices.
34	He pointed out the polling place to Roy. It was Mr. Boyd's
46	store. They walked in with confidence. Grandpop used a serious
56	voice to tell Mr. Boyd, "I want to vote." He knew voting was an
70	important job.
72	Grandpop made his choices. Then he dropped the ballot into
82	the box. But he and Roy heard noises outside the store. "What do
95	they want?" Roy thought. "Why are they annoying Grandpop on
105	voting day?" 107

B. **Read these words to yourself. Then have your partner time you. Do it two more times to see if you can beat your score!**

boil	loyal	coy	know	bird
void	oyster	foil	comb	turn
soil	choice	join	write	skirt
toy	annoy	soy	numb	her
spoil	foyer	oil	wrist	burn

Record Your Scores

Time 1: _____   Time 2: _____   Time 3: _____

At Home: Practice reading the passage above. Then create two new sentences using the words in Part B.

Name _____

> Prefixes like *un-* and *re-* are added to the beginning of a word to change its meaning. Suffixes like *-able* and *-or* are added to the end of a word to change its meaning

A. **Put the word parts together to create a whole new word.**

Example: | act | or | _actor_

1. | teach | er | _____

2. | known | un | _____

3. | mis | heard | _____

4. | soft | ly | _____

5. | re | take | _____

B. **Fill in the blanks with the word from above that makes sense.**

1. I have a question for the _____.

2. The photograph didn't come out right, so I will _____ it.

3. I think you _____ what she said.

4. The cat moved very _____ across the bed.

5. The answer to the puzzle is _____.

A. Vocabulary Words Circle the word or phrase that does not belong in the group.

1. **confidence**   coolness   calm   fear

2. **offices**   pool   trust   responsibility

3. **confused**   understand   lost   mixed-up

4. **assured**   convinced   certain   uncertain

5. **accept**   take as true   give   understand

6. Which would give you **confidence**? Tell why on the lines below.

    a. learning your lines for a play   **b.** needing your script for a play

_____

_____

B. Vocabulary Strategy: Homophones Read each sentence and look closely at the bold-faced word. Find the meaning of this word in the phrases at the right. Draw a line from the word to its meaning.

1. John feels **blue** today.   a color

    My room is painted **blue**.   a feeling of sadness

2. My aunt Sue is my favorite **aunt**.   a family member

    The tiny **ant** was carrying a crumb.   a type of insect

3. Let's **meet** at the park.   flesh from an animal that people eat

    What kind of **meat** is for dinner?   to gather; to get together

Name _____

After reading "Grandpop's Brave Choice," fill in the Character and Setting Chart.

Characters	Setting
	Time Period
	Place—Beginning of Story
	Place—Middle of Story
	Place—End of Story

Read the passage. Then complete the questions.

The First Day of School

Annie's school was being integrated. The schools for blacks and whites were going to be mixed. Annie's best friend, Joyce, had always gone to the other school, though she lived close by.

The new kids looked uncomfortable. Their clothes were dusty from the walk from their old school. Paul let a new girl sit in his chair. She looked scared and unhappy.

A teacher from the office entered quickly. "I knew it," she said. "This is a fine mess."

Miss Lloyd smiled with confidence. She said, "It might be hard for you to accept. But I assure you, it's the most joyful mess this school has ever known."

1. Underline words that have the *oy* pattern.

2. Circle the words that have prefixes or suffixes.

3. Where does the story take place?

_____

4. Name three characters in the story.

_____

5. A person who does not understand something is _____.

                                      confused   excited   assured

© Macmillan/McGraw-Hill

At Home: Reread the passage and talk about the negative effects of segregation.

Name _____

If a word ends in *-le* or *-el*, the *e* is silent. Only the *l* makes a sound.

A. Underline the *-le* and *-el* endings in the words below.

rattle	knuckle	angel	ankle	noodle
tunnel	wiggle	camel	puddle	barrel

B. Circle each word in the puzzle. Look for the *-le* and *-el* endings to help you.

a	c	r	n	o	o	k	l	e
n	a	a	a	a	t	n	n	t
k	m	t	n	t	u	u	o	w
l	e	t	g	d	n	c	o	i
e	l	l	e	p	n	k	d	g
v	a	e	l	e	e	l	l	g
c	p	u	d	d	l	e	e	l
b	a	r	r	e	l	e	f	e

C. Now use the correct words from above to complete each sentence.

1. Todd gave the baby a __ __ __ __ __ [ ] to shake.

2. Claire dug a [ ]__ __ __ __ __ in the snow and crawled into it.

3. What type of __ __[ ]__ __ __ did you put in your pasta dish?

4. They told Will to sit still, but he just had to [ ]__ __ __ __ __.

Write the letters from the boxes above to spell a secret message!

In 1879, the paper __ __ __ __l was invented.
    2 3 4 1

A. Have a partner time you as you read the passage. Record your scores below.

	Most animals need to protect themselves from possible
8	attackers. Did you know even little animals have ways to protect
19	themselves? Many will warn a larger animal first. But if the
30	bigger animal still approaches, the little animal will defend itself.
40	Ordinarily, a rattlesnake will shake its rattle before biting
49	someone. A skunk will stamp its feet or even stand on its head
62	before spraying its terrible liquid. Even a skunk does not like the
74	odor it sprays in defense. A porcupine will make its quills stand
86	up. The porcupine looks much bigger with all its quills on end!
98	The quills are also as sharp as needles! 106

Record Your Scores

First Read: Words Read _____   Time _____

Second Read: Words Read _____   Time _____

B. Partners Use this chart to check your partner's reading.

Speed	☐ too slow	☐ too fast	☐ just right
Paid attention to periods, commas, end punctuation	☐ never	☐ sometimes	☐ always
Accuracy	☐ skipped words	☐ self-corrected	☐ read every word
Read with feeling	☐ never	☐ sometimes	☐ always

© Macmillan/McGraw-Hill

At Home: Reread the passage and talk about what you learned about animal defenses.

Name _____

A **compound word** is a large word made up of two smaller words.

A. Combine these word parts to make compound words.

Example: | per | son | _person_

1. | under | ground | _____

2. | storm | thunder | _____

3. | time | summer | _____

4. | ladder | step | _____

5. | noon | after | _____

B. Use the correct words from above to complete each sentence.

1. My baby sister plays all morning and naps in the _____.

2. The rabbit dug an _____ tunnel.

3. Buck goes to the beach in the _____.

4. Molly hid under the covers when she heard the _____.

5. Mom climbed up on a _____ to change a light bulb.

Name _____

A. Vocabulary Words Check *true* or *false* for each statement.

1. If Jen's plant does not **survive**, it will die. ☐ true ☐ false

2. It is nice to **injure** a friend. ☐ true ☐ false

3. If Carl **attempts** to read a line, it means he gives up. ☐ true ☐ false

4. **Ordinarily**, you sleep when it is dark outside. ☐ true ☐ false

5. A bad **odor** will make you shut your ears. ☐ true ☐ false

B. Vocabulary Strategy: Context Clues Underline the context clues that help you figure out the vocabulary words.

A person who **attempts**, or tries, to make a garden must follow certain rules. **Ordinarily**, unless you are making a shade garden, you should plant your seeds in bright sunlight. If you do, your plants will **survive**. If you do not, they may die. You should not plant seeds in a windy place. Wind can **injure** the stems and leaves of the plants by snapping or ripping them. Place a layer of mulch over your plants, and try to ignore the bad **odor** that you smell.

Use the correct vocabulary word from above to complete each sentence.

1. The tar on the road gave off a bad _____.

2. _____, Mom drives us to school, but today we walked.

3. Living things need food, water, and a home in order to _____.

4. Pam _____ to climb the rope three times, but she cannot do it.

5. If you are not careful with newborns, you may _____ them.

© Macmillan/McGraw-Hill

Name _____

Try to find clues that will help you identify the author's purpose for writing "Big Ideas for Little Animals." Write them in the Author's Purpose Chart.

Clues	Author's Purpose

Name _____

Read the passage. Then complete the questions.

Beetles

Beetles are insects with two sets of wings and chewing mouthparts. Beetles usually lay their eggs in underground tunnels for protection.

Darkling beetles gobble up dead plants. They are ordinarily found in sandy places. Like skunks, they defend themselves by making a stinky odor.

Ladybeetles look like ladybugs, but they have 19 spots. Be careful if you catch a ladybeetle. It will not injure you, but it will leak red liquid! If you are a victim of this, you won't attempt to pick one up again!

Ladybird beetles use bright colors to warn away predators. Other beetles can hide in underbrush beneath shrubs and bushes on a butte. Beetles have many ways to survive.

1. Underline words in the passage that have -*le* or -*el* endings.

2. Circle the compound words in the passage.

3. What is the author's purpose in writing this passage?

_____

4. List one detail that the author uses to get at the purpose.

_____

5. To stay alive is to _____.

      attempt   survive   injure

At Home: Reread the passage and talk about what you learned about beetles.

© Macmillan/McGraw-Hill

Read the passage. Then complete the questions.

The Education of Joe Royal

In town, Joe Royal saw the signs "White," "Colored," and "Indian" on three sets of drinking fountains . He walked up to the one marked "Indian" and took a drink. When he turned back, his mother was holding a newspaper.

"See, Joe," she pointed to a page that read FLOYD HARPER FOR MAYOR. "This man believes in equal rights."

"Don't we have equal rights?" asked Joe.

His mother pointed to the sign. "They call it 'separate but equal.' It doesn't make me feel equal to be separate. I'm going to vote for him."

This is a character in the passage.

1. Underline details in the passage that give you clues about the setting.

2. Put a box around the characters in the passage.

3. Why does Joe's mother decide to vote for Floyd Harper for Mayor?

_____

_____

_____

_____

Read the passage. Then complete the questions.

Stinky Animals

Skunks are not the only stinky animals. A loris, a monkey-like animal that lives near deserts, makes a strong odor as a warning. If an attacker comes near it, it will make a poison to mix with its spit. A poisonous bite can make attackers very sick.

Some animals use smell to protect their space. Dogs sniff trees, fire hydrants, and shrubs to find their own smells and other odors. Tigers use a smelly liquid to mark territory as well.

Animals need all their senses to survive. They make smelly odors for protection. If you smell something funny, think carefully. It may be an animal saying, "Go away!"

1. Underline clues that support the author's purpose.

2. Write the author's purpose on the lines.

_____

3. What does the author want the reader to know?

_____

_____

_____

Name _____

When the vowel *a* comes before the letters *u, w,* and *l,* it changes its sound. Examples are *pause, saw,* and *tall.*

A. Underline the *au, aw,* and *al* patterns in the words below.

small	paw	fault	salt	haunted
lawn	straw	sidewalk	seesaw	rainfall

B. Circle each word in the puzzle. Look for the *au, aw,* and *al* patterns to help you.

r	a	i	n	f	a	l	l	n
t	l	p	m	f	a	u	l	t
r	h	a	u	n	t	e	d	s
c	l	w	w	l	a	w	n	e
s	i	d	e	w	a	l	k	e
a	i	i	s	m	a	l	l	s
l	m	a	t	k	a	i	e	a
t	h	r	s	s	t	r	a	w

C. Use the correct words from above to complete each sentence.

1. When you go up on the __ __ __|__|__ __, I go down.

2. Paul saw a monster in the __ __ __ __|__|__ __ house.

3. "It's not my __|__|__ __ __," Scott said when his brother blamed him.

4. I am big, but my little sister is __|__|__ __ __.

Write the letters from the boxes above to answer this riddle.

What travels around the world, but stays in a corner? A __ __ __ __ p.
   1 2 3 4

Name _____

A. As you read, pay attention to word accuracy.

	Long ago, the men who lived in the colonies thought, "The
11	structure of British government is flawed." What was the new
21	future that they saw for America?
27	They wrote a long letter about the king of England. They did
39	not write this foolishly. They were very careful and clear. First the
51	authors explained all the faults of the king's laws. Then they
62	explained why freedom was so important.
68	War came and the colonists won! America was free of British
79	laws. The men installed three branches of government. Each branch
89	had a job, and no single branch would be in charge of all the laws.
104	The three branches would have to work together to pass a law. 116

B. Read these words. Then have a partner time you.
Do it two more times to see if you can beat your score!

cause	claw	talk	coil	little
chalk	salt	flaw	boy	pickle
taunt	jaw	stalk	joyful	angel
crawl	lawn	halt	noisy	eagle
taught	walk	raw	annoy	tickle

Record Your Scores

Time 1: _____   Time 2: _____   Time 3: _____

© Macmillan/McGraw-Hill

At Home: Reread the passage. Then, make two sentences
using the words in Part B and see how fast you can read
them aloud.

Name _____

> When *-ment* is added to a verb, it changes the verb to a noun.
> For example, *argue* becomes *argument*.

A. Fill in the missing parts to make the bold-faced word.

1. Singing gives Jimmy a lot of **enjoyment**.

   enjoy + _____ **= enjoyment**

2. The crowd was filled with **excitement**.

   _____ **+** _____ **= excitement**

3. Did the two boys get into an **argument**?

   _____ **–** _____ **+** _____ **= argument**

4. The worker demanded **payment**.

   _____ **+** _____ **=** _____

5. Playing with my dogs gives me hours of **entertainment**.

   _____ **+** _____ **=** _____

B. Write two sentences about family. Use the word *entertainment* in one sentence. Use the word *argument* in the other.

1. _____

   _____

2. _____

   _____

Name _____

A. Vocabulary Words Circle the word or phrase that does not belong in the group.

1. developed	built	to come into being	shrink
2. foolishly	smart	silly	unwise
3. absolute	limited	total	complete
4. authored	wrote	created	painted
5. structure	arrangement	break	form

6. Joe ate a cheese sandwich, and Cathy ate a dirt pie.
   Who behaved **foolishly**? Tell why on the lines below.
   a. Joe   **b.** Cathy

_____

_____

B. Vocabulary Strategy: Word Parts Write the letter of the meaning on the right that matches the word on the left.

1. happily _____   **a.** not happy

2. happier _____   **b.** possible to count

3. unhappy _____   **c.** happy, more than someone else

4. miscount _____   **d.** in a happy way

5. countable _____   **e.** count incorrectly

As you reread "A New Government," fill in the Generalizations Chart.

Information from Text	
Prior Knowledge	
Generalization	

Read the passage. Then complete the questions.

Congress

The United States Congress is one branch of U.S. government. The Congress has a two-part structure. One part is the House of Representatives. It has a different number of members from all of the 50 states. The other part is the Senate, which has an equal number of members from each state. This structure was developed in response to the British government's mistreatment of the colonies.

The founding fathers developed this system so that neither part would have absolute power. Members of the Congress author bills. When most people in each house reach an agreement, the bill always goes to the President. The President can cancel the bill if he thinks it was foolishly written. If not, he signs it and it becomes a law.

1. Underline words with the *au*, *aw*, or *al* pattern.

2. Circle the words in the passage that contain the suffix *-ment*.

3. What generalization can you make about our government from the passage?

_____

_____

4. What is the last thing that has to happen before a bill becomes a law?

_____

5. Please behave yourself and do not act _____.

   foolishly   absolute   authored

At Home: Reread the passage and talk about what you thought was most interesting.

Name _____

The letters *o*, *ow* and *oa* can make the same sound. Examples
are *old, low,* and *road.*

**A. Draw a line under the word that best completes each sentence.
Write the word on the line.**

1. I put jelly on my _____.
   toast   town   load

2. _____ me your new bike!
   Show   Row   Slow

3. I like it when my dad lets me help him _____ the lawn.
   moan   claw   mow

4. If the fruit sits for too long, _____ will grow on it
   mold   told   sold

5. The tree trunk was _____ so a squirrel slept in it.
   foam   follow   hollow

6. I bought a _____ of bread so I could make my lunch at home.
   lack   loaf   loan

7. My favorite time of year is winter because I love _____.
   grow   snow   grew

8. Elise had to _____ notes all over town about her missing dog.
   post   bone   boast

B. Go back and circle the long *o* patterns in the answer choices.

**A. Have a partner time you as you read the passage.
Record your scores below.**

	Everyone knows what weather is. It can rain, snow, or be
11	sunny. The wind can blow harshly and knock down trees! The
22	calm glow of a sunset may follow a storm.
31	Did you know weather is created by the flow of air masses
43	in the atmosphere? Air moving over a lake or ocean picks up
55	water and can leave you soaked! Air moving over land is dry.
67	Sometimes, cool air meets warm air. This forms a cloud. If a
79	strong wind blows, it can mean that the two masses will crash.
91	This makes treacherous weather like storms and hurricanes.
99	When these storms head your way you should go to a shelter to
112	stay safe! 114

Record Your Scores

First Read: Words Read _____   Time _____

Second Read: Words Read _____   Time _____

B. Partners Use this chart to check your partner's reading.

Speed	☐ too slow	☐ too fast	☐ just right
Paid attention to periods, commas, end punctuation	☐ never	☐ sometimes	☐ always
Accuracy	☐ skipped words	☐ self-corrected	☐ read every word
Read with feeling	☐ never	☐ sometimes	☐ always

© Macmillan/McGraw-Hill

At Home: Reread the passage and talk about your favorite kind of weather.

Name _____

Looking for the open and closed syllables can help you pronounce a word correctly.

A. Which word has an open syllable? Write the word.

Example: **pumpkin**   **baker**   ___baker___

1. siren   stopwatch   _____

2. rattle   parade   _____

3. fishing   duty   _____

4. female   marker   _____

5. napkin   table   _____

B. Use the correct words from above to complete each sentence.

1. Wash your hands before you sit at the _____.

2. Mr. Kent was on cafeteria _____ every Monday.

3. A _____ deer does not have antlers.

4. Everyone in town lined the street to see the _____.

5. My mom pulls the car over when she hears a _____.

Name _____

| shelter | quarrel | destroyed | dense | treacherous |

A. Vocabulary Words: Cloze Paragraph Use the correct word from above to correctly complete each sentence.

Sometimes in nature, the weather becomes **1.** _____.

Natural disasters occur. Homes and buildings are often

2. _____. People are forced to seek **3.** _____

in places that are unfamiliar to them. These places can be

4. _____ and crowded with people. Everyone has to share

the limited space. People may **5.** _____ or argue. At times

like this, it is important for people to be kind and patient with

each other.

B. Vocabulary Strategy: Multiple-Meaning Words Use this dictionary entry to answer the questions that follow.

Which definition of bat is being used in each sentence? Circle the number that matches that definition.

bat

bat　1. (*noun*) a club used in sports to strike a ball
　　2. (*noun*) a flying mammal
　　3. (*verb*) to flutter or wink at something

1. I hit my first homerun using my lucky **bat**.
　　1　2　3

2. Watch the butterfly **bat** its wings in the breeze.
　　1　2　3

3. The **bat** flew over our heads and into the night.
　　1　2　3

© Macmillan/McGraw-Hill

Name _____

After rereading "Follow the Weather," fill in the Description Chart.

Signal Words	Descriptive Facts
	→
	→
	→
	→
	→
	→

Name _____

Read the passage. Then complete the questions.

Blizzards

When the temperature gets very low and a lot of snow falls, we call it a blizzard. The wind must blow at more than 51 miles per hour to be called a blizzard. If it is slower, it is not a blizzard. During a blizzard, the air is dense with snow. You won't be able to see very far out of your window.

It's important to know that blizzards can be treacherous. Sometimes, they have destroyed buildings, made roads impossible to travel, and blown trees down. Try not to quarrel with your family if you are snowbound. Bundle up in a warm shelter and watch the snow and the howling wind from a safe spot.

1. Underline the words that have the long *o* sound.

2. Find the multi-syllable words in the first paragraph that have closed syllables. Circle them.

3. Put a box around the signal words.

4. How will you know if there is a blizzard?

_____

5. Do not _____ with your brother.
   quarrel   dense   shelter

At Home: Reread the passage and talk about what you learned about blizzards.

© Macmillan/McGraw-Hill

Name _____

The letters *oo* can stand for the sound heard in words like *book* and *foot*.

A. Underline the *oo* pattern in the words below.

cook   foot   hoof   hood   book

wood   wool   good   shook   soot

B. Circle each word in the puzzle. Look for the letters *oo* to help you.

o	o	m	b	n	l	o	o	g
d	w	o	o	l	m	k	s	i
f	o	d	o	s	h	o	o	f
c	o	o	k	h	o	y	o	q
r	d	p	q	o	o	c	t	f
h	z	g	o	o	d	d	o	o
l	g	b	c	k	j	t	a	o
o	j	x	v	f	d	o	o	t

C. Use the correct words from above to complete each sentence.

1. Randi __ __ __ __ __ the tree, and the apples fell to the ground.

2. It was raining outside, so I put on my __ __ __ __.

3. My horse hit its __ __ __ __ on a rock, so it could not run for a week.

4. We cut the __ __ __ __ off the sheep and wove it into cloth.

Write the letters from the boxes above to spell the answer to the riddle.

What sort of star seems to speed through the air?

A __ __ __ __ ting   star!
   1 2 3 4

Name _____

A. Use this passage for a choral reading or Readers Theater.

Mr. Woods' Lesson Plan Book

5	**Monday, October 14**
8	*Note: Introduction of Jimmy Cook—new student.*
15	**Unit 6:** Clay
18	**Objective:** The students will use their artistic talent and attention
28	to detail to make chess pieces.
34	**Part I:** Hand out lumps of clay to the teams. Explain that students
47	must knead clay to work out air bubbles.
55	**Part II:**
57	• Bring out a wooden chessboard. Explain what all pieces look
67	like.
68	• Remind students that the final product must be a chessboard.
78	• Divide class into teams to make all the pieces. (Assign Brook the
90	rooks, since she likes castles. Find out which other students like
101	castles?)
102	**Part III:** Set clay chess pieces out to dry. Bake them for Wednesday's
115	class! 116

B. Read these silly sentences aloud. Pause when you see (/) and stop when you see (//). Change your voice when you see a question mark (?) or an exclamation point (!).

1. Who took/ the book?// Look,/ it was/ a crook!//

2. Can a wood hood/ look good?//

3. I'm coated/ in soot/ from head/ to foot!//

4. By the brook/ sat a cook/ with a book/ and a hook.//

At Home: Reread the silly sentences with a family member and make up some together.

Name _____

An example of a word with a prefix is *redo*. An example of a word with a suffix is *dancer*.

A. **Combine these word parts to make a word.**

Example: | un | known | _unknown_

1. | mis | heard | _____

2. | claimed | un | _____

3. | est | steep | _____

4. | ly | soft | _____

5. | ment | govern | _____

B. **Use the correct words from above to complete each sentence.**

1. The old coat was _____ at the Lost and Found desk.

2. "Please excuse me," Uncle Peter said _____.

3. In Social Studies class we learned about our _____.

4. I think I _____ you, so could you repeat yourself?

5. This was the _____ mountain the climbers had seen.

Name _____

---

revolves   filthy   common   product   introduction

A. Vocabulary Words Choose the correct word from above to complete each statement.

Example:

Neat is to *messy* as *smooth* is to <u>rumpled</u>.

1. *Soap* is to *clean* as *mud* is to _____.

2. *Gem* is to *rare* as *pebble* is to _____.

3. *End* is to *conclusion* as *beginning* is to _____.

B. Vocabulary Strategy: Analogies Underline the context clues that help you figure out the vocabulary words.

Tess gave Patrick a quick **introduction** to the basics of painting. She showed him that the big paper **revolves** around two poles. That way it is easy to get a new piece of paper to paint on. She left him to try it out on his own.

"Patrick, you're **filthy**!" she exclaimed a few minutes later. Patrick was coated in paint. "But just look at your finished **product**. What a great painting! Talent like that is rare. It is not **common** at all!"

Use the correct bold-faced word from above to complete each sentence.

1. I wished that the final _____ would be perfect.

2. All of the planets _____ around the sun.

3. "This is Patty," Dan said as an _____.

As you reread "Brook's Vase of Good Thoughts," try to find clues that will help you identify the author's purpose. Write them on the Author's Purpose Chart.

Clues	Author's Purpose

Read the passage. Then complete the questions.

A Cookie Solution

Inside a kitchen, a boy is covered in flour. His mother enters.

Kenneth: Look at me! I'm filthy. I am unable to get this cookie recipe right!

Mom: You had good grades in your cooking class. Hand me the cookbook.

[Kenneth gives it to her.]

Mom [*reading clearly*]**:** The introduction says that you need some common kitchen items. [*She looks around.*] Where is the mixer?

Kenneth: I didn't need it. Everything except the milk is in this bowl.

Mom: Good! But you must add the milk as the bowl revolves and spins around! That's your problem.

Kenneth: Thanks, Mom. I'm sure the final product will taste excellent!

[They exit.]

1. Underline the words with the *oo* pattern, as in *cook*.

2. Circle the words in the passage with prefixes or suffixes.

3. What is the author's purpose in writing this passage?

_____

4. How would you describe the ending?

_____

5. To spin around is to _____.

      product   revolve   introduce

© Macmillan/McGraw-Hill

At Home: Reread the passage with an adult, then switch roles and read it again.

Read the passage. Then complete the questions.

Monarchy

As most people know, monarchy is one of the oldest forms of government. Kings and queens still exist today in many countries around the world. England has a monarchy. But the queen has very limited power. Many people feel that the English queen is a symbol of how things used to be. Even though they have a queen, the British people rely on their democracy for laws.

Saudi Arabia also has a monarchy. This king actually rules the country. He has power over all parts of the government. He makes laws, rules over the courts, and directs the country's army.

1. Underline the following signal words in the passage:
   many   people   all

2. Put a box around the generalizations in the passage.

3. Now write a generalization about why people respect the queen of England.

   _____

   _____

Name _____

Read the passage. Then complete the questions.

An Ice Storm

One of the most treacherous weather events is an ice storm. Freezing rain falls and makes all surfaces very slippery. Frozen roadways can cause accidents.

This is a signal word.

<u>Before</u> an ice storm, make sure you have flashlights and batteries. Keep enough food for a few days. You can sprinkle things on the ground outside your house, for instance, salt or kitty litter. This might help ice melt more quickly.

During an ice storm, stay inside! Dress warmly and turn the heat down to 65 degrees. Don't take a hot shower or bath. Hot water flowing through the pipes can freeze. Stay inside until it's safe.

1. Underline the signal words or phrases that the author uses:
   before   for instance   during

2. Circle the words that describe what you should do *during* an ice storm.

3. Describe what you can do to help ice melt more quickly.

   _____

   _____

   _____

   _____

Name _____

Read the passage. Then complete the questions.

The Trip of a Lifetime

A girl and a boy are sitting outside their school.

Raina: I'm excited for the trip, aren't you?

Bradley: I was until I was told that I can't go.

Raina: Why can't you come on the trip?

Bradley: Mrs. Hood reminded me to get permission, but I forgot to get it.

Raina: So is there anything you can do so you won't miss the trip of a lifetime?

Bradley: I don't think I have much choice at this point.

Raina: Of course you do! I bet you could call home now. You could have your mom or dad let Mrs. Hood know it's okay for you to join us! What do you think?

This sentence is a clue to the author's purpose.

1. Underline two sentences that help you to understand the author's purpose.

2. Put a box around a sentence that creates excitement about what will happen.

3. Now write the author's purpose on the lines.

_____

_____

_____

A. **Which word has a prefix or suffix? Write the word and circle the prefix or suffix.**

Example: **unpinned**   **seasick**   _(unpinned)_

1. breakable   cottontail   _____

2. elephant   enjoyment   _____

3. absolute   waiter   _____

4. softly   overlook   _____

5. railroad   unsure   _____

B. **Use the correct word from above to complete each sentence.**

1. Cooking with his Dad gives Paul a lot of _____.

2. Be sure to speak _____ while you are in the library.

3. Hazel's doll was _____, so she kept it on her shelf.

4. Cal was _____ about which road led to our house.

5. The _____ will bring our desserts soon.

Name _____

> The letter *a* can have different sounds, such as in *table* and *stand*.

A. Draw a line under the word that best completes the sentence. Write the word on the line.

1. When it is cold outside, I wear a _____.
   snap   hat   ray

2. I wrote my name at the top of the _____.
   page   glass   tape

3. Eric _____ when the play was over.
   raked   clapped   gabbed

4. We had indoor recess because it _____.
   paid   rained   failed

5. _____ to her so that she will see us.
   Wait   Tap   Wave

6. Jon and Tara boarded the _____ to go on their honeymoon.
   plan   plane   plain

7. Can you _____ the ball to Jack next?
   pass   pat   pill

8. The bed was 30 years old, so they bought a new _____.
   march   microphone   mattress

B. Circle the long *a* words, such as *table*. Put a box around the short *a* words, such as *strand*.

A. As you read, pay attention to punctuation, intonation, pauses, and stops.

	Have you ever asked, "What's the coldest place on Earth?" The
11	North and South Poles are coldest. The weather there is frequently
22	harsh, and few people live there all year. Snow and ice cover most of
36	the land.
38	In the past, traveling to Antarctica was unsafe. Waves and
48	wind could destroy boats. Ships were trapped by ice. Today, ships
59	frequently travel to Antarctica. The conditions are the same, but
69	we are now better able to handle them. Also, sailors are more aware
82	and careful. Sailors say, "Be prepared for the raging seas! Travel in
94	the summer only!"
97	Antarctica's landscape is always changing. Ice sheets break off and
107	crash into the sea, or float nearby and become part of the land. 120

B. Read these words to yourself. Then have your partner time you. Do it two more times to see if you can beat your score!

rain	stay	grab	book	hoof
clap	wave	slam	took	elbow
snap	mat	paper	good	owner
brand	clad	lamp	wool	grow
hat	flag	table	cook	shadow

Record Your Scores

Time 1: _____   Time 2: _____   Time 3: _____

At Home: Reread the pasage to an adult, then write a sentence using two of the words on the list.

Name _____

Use **prefixes**, **suffixes**, and **endings** to change the meaning of a word.

A. Use the puzzle pieces to form a word.

Example:

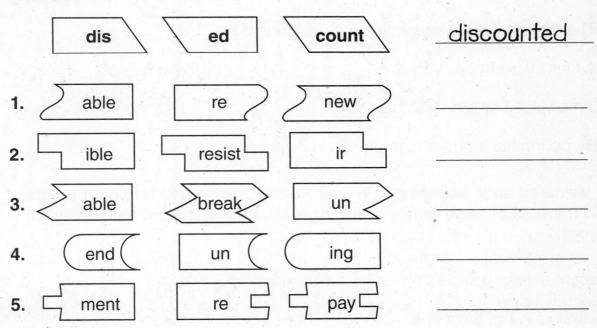

| dis | ed | count | _discounted_ |

1. able   re   new   _____

2. ible   resist   ir   _____

3. able   break   un   _____

4. end   un   ing   _____

5. ment   re   pay   _____

B. Use the correct words from above to complete each sentence.

1. Jake thanked May for her _____ of the loan.

2. The plastic serving dish is _____.

3. The _____ scent of chocolate-chip cookies drifted from the kitchen.

4. Jan's library card is _____.

5. The movie was so long that it seemed _____.

| extreme | frequently | harsh | uninhabited | contacting | enables |

A. Vocabulary Words: Cloze Sentences Use the correct word from above to complete each sentence.

1. During a blizzard, the weather is _____.

2. The sound of squeaky chalk on a chalkboard is _____.

3. As far as we know, Venus is _____ by living beings.

4. Jane visits her grandmother _____.

5. By calling his friend on the phone, Hal was _____ him.

B. Vocabulary Strategy: Word Parts Read each family of words. Find the root of each family at the right. Draw a line from the family to its root.

1. actor, acting, acted   a. note

2. repay, paying, payment   b. use

3. cooker, cooking, uncooked   c. act

4. notable, denote, noted   d. cook

5. usable, misuse, user   e. pay

© Macmillan/McGraw-Hill

Name _____

As you reread "The Loneliest Place on Earth," fill in the Problem and
Solution Map to help you understand the selection.

Problem

Attempt		Outcome
	→	

Attempt		Outcome
	→	

Attempt		Outcome
	→	

Solution

Name _____

Read the passage. Then complete the questions.

The Arctic Tern

The Arctic tern migrates farther than other birds. It flies from the North Pole to the South Pole each year! An airplane would take more than a month to travel that far. A trip that long world be unworkable. Arctic terns fly so frequently that they barely stop to land. They spend summers at the poles and lay eggs in the Arctic. They migrate to avoid the harsh, extreme conditions in the winter.

People who live near the poles and need to find food follow the terns. If an area is inhabited by many terns, they know that there are many fish. Fish are a renewable food source. Tracking terns enables many native people to eat.

1. Underline words with long *a*, such as *table*. Circle words with short *a*, such as *stand*.

2. Put a box around 3-syllable words with prefixes, suffixes, or inflectional endings.

3. What is a problem that people who live near the poles have?

   _____

4. What is the solution?

   _____

5. I use the phone when _____ someone.
      contacting   pushing   swimming

At Home: Reread the passage and talk about what you learned about the Arctic tern.

Name _____

The letter *i* can have different sounds, such as in *mine* and *limit*.

A. Underline the long *i* words, such as *mine*, and circle the short *i* words, such as *limit*.

bike   kite   mice   basic   pick

insect   pinch   hint   arrive   inside

B. Read the clues. Then use the words to complete the sentences.

Across

1. I taught my sister how to do a __ dive.

2. It is cold outside but warm __.

3. When it is a windy day, I fly my __.

4. It is not nice to __ your brother.

5. Our cat loves to chase the __ in the barn.

Down

1. After you are done playing, __ up your toys.

2. Did Jen and Kim __ at the birthday party together?

3. A beetle is a type of __.

4. I will not tell you the answer but I can give you a __.

5. I like to ride my __.

Name _____

**A. Have a partner time you as you read the passage.
Record your scores below.**

	Kim and Nila are miserable. They are tired of the dinners
11	they have had recently. They say, "These meals are boring!"
21	They miss the fatty foods they ate before their dad became ill.
33	They both know it is better to eat healthful foods. So Kim wants
46	to prepare a special dish they will all like. What should she make
59	that will taste good but still be healthy?
67	Kim is eager to please her parents. She goes into the kitchen
79	and Nila follows. The sisters ask each other, "What different
89	ingredients can we combine?" While Kim looks for baking
98	equipment, Nila decides that she wants peppermint ice cream.
107	Maybe Kim will find a special spice in the back cabinet! 118

Record Your Scores

First Read: Words Read _____   Time _____

Second Read: Words Read _____   Time _____

B. Partners Use this chart to check your partner's reading.

Speed	☐ too slow	☐ too fast	☐ just right
Paid attention to periods, commas, end punctuation	☐ never	☐ sometimes	☐ always
Accuracy	☐ skipped words	☐ self-corrected	☐ read every word
Read with feeling	☐ never	☐ sometimes	☐ always

© Macmillan/McGraw-Hill

At Home: Reread the passage and talk about your favorite dessert.

Name _____

Use -*tion* and -*sion* at the end of a word to change its meaning.

A. Fill in the missing parts to make the bold-faced word.

1. There needs to be a **separation** between the two desks.

   _____ – _____ + _____ = **separation**

2. The evil man finally gave his **confession**.

   _____ + _____ = _____

3. This misunderstanding led to his **confusion**.

   _____ – _____ + _____ = _____

4. I do a great **imitation** of a tiger.

   _____ – _____ + _____ = _____

5. The teacher wanted each of her students to get a good **education**.

   _____ – _____ + _____ = _____

B. Write two sentences about school. Use the word *separation* **in
one sentence. Use the word** *education* **in the other.**

1. _____

   _____

2. _____

   _____

| miserable | eager | grumbled | suggested | compressed |

A. Vocabulary Words: Cloze Sentences Use the correct word to complete each sentence.

1. Grandpa _____ when he did not get his dinner.

2. Joe _____ that we go to the park since it was a nice day.

3. Kelly is _____ because she is too sick to go to Todd's party.

4. I was so _____ to swim that I forgot to take my glasses off before I jumped in!

5. I _____ the pages together so the folder would be flat.

B. Vocabulary Strategy: Dictionary Use this dictionary entry to answer the questions that follow.

1. Where does the word **miserable** come from?

   _____

   _____

2. Which Latin word did the word **miserable** come from?

   _____

3. According to the word origin, what does **miser** mean?

   _____

> **miserable**
>
> **mis·er·a·ble** *adj.* **1.** Very uncomfortable or unhappy **2.** Causing or having great discomfort or distress
>
> [Middle English, from Old French, from Latin word "miser," meaning poor.]

Name _____

Reread "The Perfect Ingredient," and fill in the Theme Chart.

What Does the Character Do and Say?	What Happens to the Character?

Author's Purpose

© Macmillan/McGraw-Hill

Name _____

Read the passage. Then complete the questions.

Pike's Dinner Party

Pike was a nice little elf. He invited his relations to dinner. Eager to make a good meal, he made a list of things to get.

To his surprise, he found butter beside a cow! Pike took it with him. He then found fish and spices nearby, too.

He went home to cook.

When they arrived, his guests grumbled to each other.

"Why are you miserable?" Pike asked them in confusion.

"Someone took our food!" they said.

Pike looked uncomfortable, and then he suggested, "Let's have dinner."

To their surprise, their food was on the table! Pike's relations came to the conclusion that Pike made a mistake. They knew he only wanted to be nice by cooking for them, so they all decided to forgive him.

1. Underline words that have the long *i* vowel sound.

2. Circle words that have the suffixes *-tion* or *-sion*.

3. Why were the guests miserable?

_____

4. What is the theme of the story?

_____

_____

5. Most children are _____ to be called on when they know the answer.
      miserable   eager   grumbled

At Home: Reread the passage and talk about what kind of friend Pike is.

Read the passage. Then complete the questions.

Traveling to Antarctica

Getting to Antarctica can take a long time. It is impossible to visit in the winter because the pack ice is too thick. Only one airline flies people near Antarctica. But, it only gives people a view from the plane.

Therefore, if you plan to visit, go between October and March. Ships take passengers on tours, making stops on land. It takes about two days to get there. Then, it takes about four more days to visit all the places. Getting to Antarctica costs a lot, so some people go as research assistants. Though they must work, it is cheaper to visit.

This is a problem in the passage.

This is a signal word.

1. Underline the following signal words in the passage:
   because   therefore   so

2. Put a box around two problems in the passage.

3. Now write the solutions to the problems.

   _____

   _____

   _____

   _____

   _____

Name _____

Read the passage. Then complete the questions.

The Red Hen Today

A red hen found some wheat seeds. "Who will help me plant these?" she asked.

This sentence tells something the red hen does.

The dog said, "I'm too sleepy."

So she planted them. They grew very tall. "Who will help me harvest the wheat?" she asked.

The cat said, "Get lost."

She harvested it and made some flour. "Who will help me make the bread?" she asked.

The horse was on his cell phone. So, he didn't even answer her.

When the bread came out of the oven, it smelled delicious. The animals begged for some bread. The hen just said, "You think this smells good? I'm making waffles tomorrow!"

1. Underline the things that the characters say in the passage.

2. Put a box around the things the little red hen does.

3. Now write the theme of the passage on the lines:

_____

_____

Name _____

> The letter *e* can have different sounds, such as in *week* and *wet*.

A. **Underline the long and short e sounds in the words below.**

speed	cents	green	step	leash
dress	teach	shell	slept	teeth

B. **Circle each word in the puzzle. Look for the letter e to help you.**

g	d	s	s	s	k	s	t	s
r	g	h	p	s	s	t	e	p
d	r	e	s	s	l	e	c	l
e	e	l	p	s	e	a	m	e
n	e	l	e	n	p	c	m	a
s	n	t	e	e	t	h	s	s
k	n	b	d	x	a	c	h	h
x	d	c	e	n	t	s	f	t

C. **Use the correct words from above to complete each sentence.**

1. This pen cost me twenty-five ⬜_ __ __ __.

2. I picked up a __⬜_ __ __ __ from the beach and held it to my ear.

3. My dad drove the car when the light turned __ __ __⬜_.

4. Little Red Riding Hood __ __⬜_ __ __ in the little bear's bed.

Write the letters from the boxes above on the lines. It spells the answer to the riddle!

Who should you never play cards with in the jungle?

A __ __ __ __ tah!
   1 2 3 4

Name _____

A. As you read, pay attention to word accuracy.

	On a breezy summer day, step into a garden or forest. See if
13	you can find a serene place to rest. The sweet smells and fresh creek
27	water can make you feel terrific! But plants have another way to heal
40	people. Do you know what it is?
47	Many medicines come from plants and flowers. Scientists study
56	plants to find cures for illnesses. Some healing fluids are pressed
67	or squeezed out of plant stems or leaves. Sometimes, leaves are
78	brewed in a tea. It is not always easy to find a plant that can heal a
95	certain disease. Scientists must use precise measurements and careful
104	preparation. They must also make sure that the medicines are safe for
116	people. 117

B. Read these words to yourself. Then have a partner time you. Do it two more times to see if you can beat your score!

sweet	nest	feast	bright	tilt
sleep	step	tent	packet	tray
bless	peel	treat	twist	gain
creep	sled	free	shrink	cliff
empty	beep	next	slime	stable

Record Your Scores

Time 1: _____   Time 2: _____   Time 3: _____

At Home: Reread the passage then create three sentences using the words from the list.

© Macmillan/McGraw-Hill

If you know the meaning of a word's root, you can figure out the meaning of the word.

A. Which word has a Latin root? You can use a dictionary to help you.

Example:

proceed	profound	_proceed_
1. refer	reduce	_____
2. produce	pronoun	_____
3. recede	reclaim	_____
4. super	succeed	_____
5. introduce	interpret	_____

B. Use the correct word from above to complete each sentence.

1. Beth feared she would fail, but then she saw she would _____!

2. The teacher said she would _____ our workload.

3. Wow! How did you _____ such a fine story?

4. After the ocean began to _____, they could see shells on the beach.

5. I would like to _____ you to my sister, Polly.

Name _____

| reduce | available | scents | precise | preparation |

A. Vocabulary Words: Cloze Paragraph Use the correct word from above to complete each sentence.

Baking an apple pie takes a lot of **1.** _____. You

must measure out **2.** _____ amounts of each thing that

you put in it. Use the right ingredients, too. Do not just use whatever is

3. _____ in your house. To **4.** _____ baking

time, make the crust very thin. That will help it bake quickly. Then the

sweet **5.** _____ of apple and crust will fill your home.

B. Vocabulary Strategy: Thesaurus Use this thesaurus entry to answer the questions that follow.

precious/prelude

precious [adj] *extremely valuable*
  dearest, prized, treasured
  ANT worthless, valueless, useless

precise [adj] *exactly or sharply defined*
  careful, exact, fixed, specific
  ANT imprecise, unclear, vague

predict [v] *think of an outcome*
  forecast, foresee, guess, suppose

prefer [v] *single out*
  desire, pick, select, wish

prelude [n] *beginning of event*
  introduction, preface, start
  ANT end, ending, finale, finish

1. What are the guide words on this page?

_____

2. List two antonyms for the word **precise**.

_____

3. Which of the following means the opposite of **prelude**: *preface, beginning,* or *finale*?

_____

© Macmillan/McGraw-Hill

As you reread "Plants That Can Heal," fill in the Cause and Effect Chart
to figure out what happened and why.

Cause	→	Effect
	→	
	→	
	→	
	→	

Read the passage. Then complete the questions.

Tea Tree Oil

Tea tree oil is a medicine that comes from plants. Its discovery made scientists cheerful because of its many uses. It can reduce infection and disease that comes from dirty, untreated cuts. Tea tree oil comes from one of the species of tea tree plant. People steam the leaves in order to release the oil.

Tea tree oil has a strong, sharp scent. Some think it might make one's mouth smell fresh and clean. However, if you proceed to eat or drink tea tree oil, it can make you very sick.

Tea tree oil is available in many creams, toothpastes, and gels. Scientists use precise amounts, especially in the preparation of tooth cleaning products.

1. Underline words in the second paragraph with the long *e* sound.

2. Circle the words in the passage with the Latin roots *duc* and *ceed*.

3. If you put tea tree oil on a cut, what will happen?

_____

4. What will happen if you drink tea tree oil?

_____

5. Different perfumes can have very different _____.

ducts   cents   scents

© Macmillan/McGraw-Hill

At Home: Reread the passage with an adult and talk about what you think is most interesting about tea tree oil.

The letter *o* may sound different in different words. Examples are *home* and *hop*.

A. Underline the words with long *o*, as in *home*. Circle the words with short *o*, as in *hop*.

float	smock	bowl	poem	knob
popcorn	spot	smoke	solar	sob

B. Circle each word in the puzzle. Look for the letter *o* to help you.

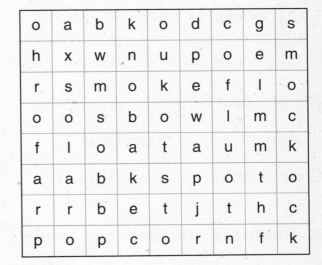

o	a	b	k	o	d	c	g	s
h	x	w	n	u	p	o	e	m
r	s	m	o	k	e	f	l	o
o	o	s	b	o	w	l	m	c
f	l	o	a	t	a	u	m	k
a	a	b	k	s	p	o	t	o
r	r	b	e	t	j	t	h	c
p	o	p	c	o	r	n	f	k

C. Use the correct words from above to complete each sentence.

1. To stay clean while painting, Joe wears a __ __ __ [ ] __ .

2. We snacked on __ [ ] __ __ __ __ during the movie.

3. The logs burned brightly, and __ [ ] __ __ __ rose up into the chimney.

4. Jan ate her oatmeal out of a [ ] __ __ __ .

Write the letters from the boxes above to spell out the answer to the riddle.

What has teeth but cannot eat? A __ __ __ __ !
1 2 3 4

A. Have a partner time you as you read the passage.
Record your scores below.

	Joe and Nicole have a homework assignment over the long
10	weekend. They must find something that is important to their
20	family history. Joe thinks, "This will be fun!" Nicole just wants
31	to finish the project.
35	They go home and climb the irregular attic stairs. They look
46	all over and find old toys. Then, in a hole in the floor they find an
62	old bottle. The bottle has a note folded up inside it. Joe says,
75	"It might be a map to a treasure!" Nicole says, "Oh, it's just an
89	old bottle." Is it an object they can use, or just a boring bottle?
103	The note inside it is in a sort of code. Can they break the code? 118

Record Your Scores

First Read: Words Read _____ Time _____

Second Read: Words Read _____ Time _____

B. Partners Use this chart to check your partner's reading.

Speed	☐ too slow	☐ too fast	☐ just right
Paid attention to periods, commas, end punctuation	☐ never	☐ sometimes	☐ always
Accuracy	☐ skipped words	☐ self-corrected	☐ read every word
Read with feeling	☐ never	☐ sometimes	☐ always

© Macmillan/McGraw-Hill

At Home: Reread the passage with a family member and talk about what family object you might share with your class.

Name _____

> Use the prefixes *im-*, *in-*, and *ir-* to change the word to mean its opposite. For example, *pure* becomes *impure*.

A. Fill in the missing parts to make the bold-faced word.

1. Lola was **impatient** for the class to begin.

   im + _____ = **impatient**

2. The lazy cat was plump and **inactive**.

   in + _____ = **inactive**

3. The shirt was not a standard size because it was **irregular**.

   ir + _____ = **irregular**

4. Gravity is an **invisible** force.

   in + _____ = **invisible**

5. This puzzle is so hard, it is **impossible** to solve.

   im + _____ = **impossible**

B. Write two sentences about the weekend. Use the word *impossible* in one sentence. Use the word *inactive* in the other.

1. _____

   _____

2. _____

   _____

Name _____

A. Vocabulary Words Check *true* or *false* for each statement.

1. Wearing shorts in cold weather is **inappropriate**. ☐true ☐false

2. If you are waiting **impatiently**, you are calm. ☐true ☐false

3. A **treasure** is usually junk you can throw away. ☐true ☐false

4. If something is **irregular**, it is unusual. ☐true ☐false

5. Each of us deals with different **situations** in our lives. ☐true ☐false

B. Vocabulary Strategy: Context Clues Underline the context clues that help you figure out the vocabulary words.

Tapping her feet and whistling, Jan was **impatiently** waiting. It was almost her turn to be on stage at the school play. Jan wore an oddly shaped, **irregular** shirt. She was playing a **treasure** hunter. She looked through a box for gold and jewels. She walked on stage with a rude, **inappropriate** look on her face. She had to act in different scenes and **situations**. Even though Jan did a few things wrong, the audience cheered at the end of the play.

Use the correct vocabulary word from above to complete each sentence.

1. It is _____ to chew with your mouth open.

2. You can often find a family _____ in an attic or basement.

3. Books show characters in different _____.

4. The sweater was on sale because it was _____.

5. Stan waited _____ for his friend to call.

© Macmillan/McGraw-Hill

Name _____

Reread "Joe and Nicole Crack the Code." Fill in the Author's Perspective Chart to determine the author's point of view.

Clues	Author's Perspective

ame _____

Read the passage. Then complete the questions.

A Code for Cole

Miss Joss's class was studying situations when people used codes. "Long ago, a sailor sent this message to his friends:

Last for the sea was you, dear Rose!

"The sailor's friends left to meet him right away. So, what do you think he was telling them?" asked Miss Joss.

Cole wasn't well-behaved in class. He often made inappropriate noises or tapped impatiently while other students worked on problems. But today he raised his hand. "Treasure!" he said, once Miss Joss called on him. "The clue is 'last.' The last letter in each of those words spells out 'treasure' when you put them together."

"Fine work, Cole! The Rose was a ship that sank. Divers fetched gems from it and made a fortune!"

1. Underline words with the long *o* sound. Circle words with the short *o* sound.

2. Put a box around any words with a prefix.

3. What are some clues to the author's perspective?

_____

_____

4. What is the author's perspective?

_____

_____

5. It is rude to make _____ noises.
   impatiently   irregular   inappropriate

At Home: Reread the passage and talk about what you would like to find in a treasure.

Name _____

The letters *oo* can make two different sounds. They can make the sound in the word *took* or the sound in the word *stool*.

A. Draw a line under the word that best completes each sentence. Write the word on the line.

1. Late at night, I look into the dark sky and see the _____.

   stoop   moon   sloop

2. Go to your cubby and hang your coat on a _____.

   hoot   hook   harp

3. I did not want my feet to get cool and wet, so I wore _____.

   bowls   books   boots

4. When it is hot outside, Bobby goes for a swim in the _____.

   pool   poodle   pot

5. I'm sorry! Did I just step on your _____?

   foul   fool   foot

6. My _____ was not tied so the wind whipped across my face.
   room   hood   scoop

7. The _____ in the delivery room was very happy.
   moo   mood   mole

8. Terry didn't have any _____ at home, so she bought her lunch.

   food   fool   bloom

B. Go back and circle the *oo* pattern in the answer choices above.

A. Use this passage for a choral reading or Readers Theater.

Whale Watch on *The Mongoose*

5	• There is plenty of room on the smooth-sailing *Mongoose*. We
16	have room for up to 50 people.
22	• Whale Watches are from noon to 7 P.M. every night. We have
33	moonlight cruises, too.
36	• Visit the Whale Watch museum to see harpoons and a real
47	whale's tooth!
49	What should you bring?
53	• On day cruises, we provide delicious cookies and juice.
62	• On evening cruises, snack food is provided at no cost.
72	• Wear a good waterproof rain slicker with a hood because you
83	will probably get wet!
87	• On winter cruises, wear a good wool sweater. It can get cool at
100	night.
101	You can depend on *The Mongoose* for the best whale watch deal! 113

B. Read these silly sentences aloud. Pause when you see (/) and stop when you see (//). Change your voice when you read a question mark (?) or an exclamation point (!).

1. Oops!// Did the goofy goose/ drink the whole pool?//

2. Look at the/ sooty hoof!// It is the foot/ of a moose.//

3. "Boo hoo!"/ whooped the baboon.// "I have shampoo/ on my tooth!"//

4. A kangaroo zoomed/ across the room/ and shook its foot/ at a loose balloon.//

5. Can you woof/ like a snoozing crook?//

© Macmillan/McGraw-Hill

At Home: Reread the passage with a friend and talk about what you learned about *The Mongoose*.

Name _____

When a vowel is followed by the letter *r*, its sound changes, as in *for* or *car*.

A. Which word has an *r*-controlled vowel?

Example:

personal	family	<u>personal</u>
1. repetition	important	_____
2. argument	rhythm	_____
3. dragonfly	grandfather	_____
4. rainforest	jackrabbit	_____
5. right	hamburger	_____

B. Use the correct word from above to complete each sentence.

1. Mark and I made up after our _____, and I forgave him.

2. Lots of interesting animals live in the _____.

3. Be sure to write this down, because it is very _____.

4. At the barbecue, I ate a _____.

5. Todd likes it when his _____ tells stories from long ago.

Name _____

A. Vocabulary Words Circle the word or phrase that does not belong in the group.

1. **delicious**	tasteless	yummy	tasty
2. **vanished**	leave	fade away	appear
3. **reflection**	mirror	darkness	pond
4. **majesty**	queen	humble	greatness
5. **depend**	distrust	rely	count on

6. Who would you rather **depend** on? Tell why on the lines below.
   a. your best friend   **b.** a monster

_____

_____

B. Vocabulary Strategy: Word Parts Write the letter of the word on the right that matches the meaning on the left.

1. to agree to pay for and receive ____   **a.** attract

2. to draw attention away from ____   **b.** inscribe

3. to write in something ____   **c.** distract

4. a person who writes in things ____   **d.** subscribe

5. to draw close to ____   **e.** scribe

Name _____

Use this Summary Chart to retell "Proof of Goodness" in your own words.

Beginning

Middle

End

Summary

Name._____

Read the passage. Then complete the questions.

A Whale Helps Cooper

Cooper and his dad saw the reflection of the moon on the water from their boat. Soon, they were sailing smoothly. The sun was rising in all its majesty. Cooper caught a striped bass. It would be delicious when they cook it for dinner.

Cooper looked around. The land seemed to have vanished! They hadn't checked the weather report! Good sailors depend on it to warn of danger.

A whale rose out of the water, its eye fixed on Cooper. "Let's follow it," said Cooper. Soon, they saw land! Cooper and his dad zoomed in to shore. They promised never to be foolish again.

1. Underline words in the passage that have the *oo* pattern.

2. Circle the multi-syllable words that contain an *r*-controlled vowel.

3. Summarize the first paragraph in one short sentence.

_____

4. Summarize the last paragraph in one short sentence.

_____

5. I _____ on my parents for many things.
   delicious   reflection   depend

At Home: Read the passage aloud and talk about your favorite part.

Name _____

Read the passage. Then complete the questions.

Terrific Ideas from Nature

We get many great ideas from nature.
Beavers have made dams for many years.
They make them in order to stop the flow
of water and form a pond or small lake.
Humans do the same thing! We create dams
to stop water so we can use it in our homes.
We can even make electricity with the
water's movement!

Birds gather sticks and twigs to form a nest. As a result, the nest
helps keep their eggs warm and comfortable. Our beds are similar
to nests. The first mattresses for humans were even stuffed with
straw!

1. Underline the following words or signal phrases in the passage:
   in order to   so   as a result

2. Put a box around the causes in the passage.

3. What is the effect of the event described in the following
   sentence: *Humans create dams*? Write your answer on
   the lines.

   _____

   _____

   _____

© Macmillan/McGraw-Hill

Name _____

Read the passage. Then complete the questions.

A Camping Trip

Simone and her friends went camping. They pitched the tents and then sat down to talk. They sang their favorite songs and told scary stories. Finally, it was time for bed, but Simone and Cass were not tired.

> This is a part of the passage you can ask questions about to discover the author's perspective.

"I know," said Cass. "Let's use our flashlights! Jenna and I have used Morse code a few times to send messages." Cass poked her head out and flashed her light on Jenna's tent. "I just told Jenna to wake up!" she said laughing.

Then, Jenna flashed her light on Simone's tent to respond. Cass said, "I'll translate for you. Jenna told us to leave her alone!" Simone laughed quietly. "I guess we should let the others sleep now."

1. Put a box around parts of the passage you can ask questions about to discover the author's perspective.

2. Now write one question on the line.

_____

3. Now write the answer on the line.

_____

_____

_____

Name _____

Read the passage. Then complete the questions.

Visiting the Whales

Whenever Jeff stayed at his grandmother's house for a weekend, he spent Sunday at the lagoon. Huge baleen whales often came close to the edge of the water. When he was small, he thought they were the same whales each visit. Later he realized that the friendly whales migrated and that different whales arrived each time.

This weekend the whales were traveling south with their newborn calves! The baby whales stuck close by the bodies of their mothers. Jeff watched as the spotty gray backs rose out of the water and sank back in. Soon, the whales had vanished into the deep water.

This sentence tells an event.

1. Underline an important event in the first paragraph.

2. Draw a box around one event in the second paragraph.

3. Now write a summary of the passage on the lines.

_____

_____

_____

_____

_____

_____

Name _____

A. Combine the word parts to make a word.

Example: | use | | mis | __misuse__

1. | im | | perfect | _____

2. | sion | | conclu | _____

3. | ability | | in | _____

4. | vaca | | tion | _____

5. | locked | | un | _____

B. Fill in the blanks with the word from above that makes sense.

1. Did Nicole leave the door _____?

2. Carter's _____ to run quickly made him finish last in the race.

3. The napkin holder was _____, but Kate's mom still liked it!

4. The book had such a good _____ that I was excited for Iris to finish reading it.

5. Are you going to the beach with us for a _____?

Name _____

The schwa is a vowel sound that sounds like "uh." It can be heard in words such as *waiter*, *angel*, and *bubble*.

A. Underline the syllable with the schwa sound in the words below.

wooden   apple   saddles   motor   needles

letters   bagel   slogan   older   better

B. Read the clues. Then use the words to complete the sentences.

Across

1. That car has a powerful __.

2. Jim uses __ and thread to make quilts.

3. Connor is two years __ than Nicholas.

4. Do you want an __ or an orange?

5. A word is made of many __.

Down

1. I took a log and carved a __ doll from it.

2. Mine was good, but yours was even __.

3. They bought __ so we could ride the horses.

4. I ate a __ for breakfast.

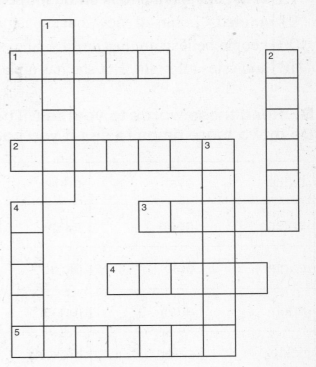

A. As you read, pay attention to pauses, stops, and end punctuation.

	Arden is a young girl who can communicate with animals. She
11	is able to help shepherds and farmers tend their animals, but the
23	people won't listen to her.
28	No one in her town believes her. She tells the king and queen,
41	"I can talk to animals and help everyone get along." The king and
54	queen say, "You're telling lies!" They send her away.
63	As she walks through the bustling streets, she sees that a horse
75	is in pain and a bird is afraid for her eggs. She tries to explain the
91	animals' points of view, but she is put in jail for telling what the
105	people believe are just stories. She is miserable about her situation
116	and cries all night. But she has a plan! 125

B. Read these words to yourself. Then have your partner time you. Do it two more times to see if you can beat your score!

battle	ever	riddle	look	shook
enter	open	taken	soot	pool
eagle	able	pickle	hoot	roof
ripen	after	funnel	loop	hoof
tickle	safer	broken	tool	cook

Record Your Scores

Time 1: _____   Time 2: _____   Time 3: _____

At Home: Reread the passage and talk about the benefits of Arden's talent.

© Macmillan/McGraw-Hill

Name _____

When -*ant* is added to the end of a word, it can change the meaning of the word. An example is *ignore* becomes *ignorant*.

A. Fill in the missing parts to make the word in bold.

1. Why are you so **hesitant** to do what you are told?

   hesitate − _____ + _____ = **hesitant**

2. Pay attention, because this is very **important**.

   _____ + _____ = **important**

3. Jane will do magic, and Paul will be her **assistant**.

   _____ + _____ = _____

4. The **attendant** in the parking lot smiled at us.

   _____ + _____ = _____

5. **Pollutants** in the water can harm animals and humans.

   _____ − _____ + _____ + _____ = _____

B. Write two sentences about feelings. Use the word *important* in one sentence. Use the word *hesitant* in the other.

1. _____

   _____

2. _____

   _____

A. Vocabulary Words Circle the word or phrase in the group that does not belong with the bold-faced word.

1. **peculiar**	strange	normal	odd
2. **bustling**	silent	busy	lively
3. **communicate**	write	speak	move
4. **innocent**	at fault	harmless	blameless
5. **deserve**	earn	waste	worthy of

6. Which is more **peculiar**? Tell why on the lines below.
   a. a human boy from Planet Earth   **b.** a space boy from Planet Mars

_____

_____

B. Vocabulary Strategy: Homophones Read each sentence and look closely at the bold-faced word. Find the meaning of this word in the phrases at the right. Draw a line from the sentence to its meaning.

1. Do you think my hand will **heal**?   the back of a foot
   I bumped my **heel** on the step.   to become healthy again

2. After I run far, I feel **weak**.   not so strong
   Jed stayed at Tom's house for a **week**!   seven days

3. **Hi**! My name is Polly.   the opposite of low
   Rupert cannot reach that **high**.   a greeting; hello

Name _____

As you reread "The Girl Who Talked to Animals," write one event in each box of the Sequence Chart below.

Event

↓

↓

↓

Name _____

Read the passage. Then complete the questions.

A New Princess for Prince Aiden

A new princess was coming to meet Prince Aiden. The ballroom was bustling. A trumpet blew and Princess Isabel walked in with four attendants.

They were seated and the show began. Bored, Isabel fell asleep.

A jester juggled ten blue bottles. Prince Aiden stepped down to communicate with the juggler.

"Can you teach me that?" he asked.

"Sure!" said the jester. "I'm Lauren. I don't deserve your company." Everyone in attendance watched as Lauren showed Aiden her tricks. King Steven smiled, for he knew that innocent little Lauren was a princess, too! So Prince Aiden married Princess Lauren while Isabel slept.

1. Underline words with the schwa sound heard with -*el*, -*le*, -*er*, or -*en*.

2. Circle five sets of homophones in the passage.

3. What happened right after the trumpet blew?

_____

4. What happened right before the jester began to juggle?

_____

5. Robin did not do anything wrong, so she is _____.

                    peculiar   bustling   innocent

© Macmillan/McGraw-Hill

At Home: Reread the passage and talk about the order of events.

Name _____

Sometimes the letters *ow* and *ou* make the sound heard in *brownie* and *sound*.

A. Underline the words with the *ow* pattern. Put a box around the words with the *ou* pattern.

bow	loud	towel	owl	crown
scout	town	now	pound	clown

B. Circle each word in the puzzle. Look for the letters *ou* and *ow* to help you.

c	a	t	p	l	b	t	r	a
s	c	o	u	t	t	o	s	c
l	x	w	e	n	o	w	r	r
o	n	e	b	o	w	l	o	o
u	c	l	o	w	n	l	u	w
d	n	b	w	n	m	t	t	n
s	p	o	u	n	d	w	f	t

C. Now use the correct words from above to complete each sentence.

1. John will __ __ __ __ __ out the trail to make sure it is safe.

2. At Jo's party, we will have __ __ __ __ __ cake for dessert.

3. The queen wore a __ __ __ __ __ on her head.

4. __ __ __ it is time to finish your homework.

Write the letters from the boxes above on the lines below to answer the riddle.

What is full of holes, but still holds water?

A __ __ __ __ ge!
    1 2 3 4

© Macmillan/McGraw-Hill

Name _____

**A. Have a partner time you as you read the passage.
Record your scores below.**

	Becky, Lance, and their Uncle Logan are out on a camping
11	trip. Becky's mom and dad helped them set up the tent, but they
24	were not going to camp with them. They were going to stay at a
38	hotel nearby. Uncle Logan is a camping pro. The kids tell each
50	other, "We know we're secure with him."
57	Lance and Uncle Logan make jokes. Becky says, "I don't think
68	those jokes are funny!" She pouts. Becky asks, "What are you so
80	proud about?"
82	She wishes to be alone, so she walks away. She is caught in a
96	terrible downpour! The ground gives way beneath her and she slips
107	down the side of a hill. She is surrounded by mounds of mud. She
121	fears she will drown! 125

Record Your Scores

First Read: Words Read _____   Time _____

Second Read: Words Read _____   Time _____

B. Partners Use this chart to check your partner's reading.

Speed	☐ too slow	☐ too fast	☐ just right
Paid attention to periods, commas, end punctuation	☐ never	☐ sometimes	☐ always
Accuracy	☐ skipped words	☐ self-corrected	☐ read every word
Read with feeling	☐ never	☐ sometimes	☐ always

© Macmillan/McGraw-Hill

At Home: Reread the passage, then talk about what you think will happen.

Some words can come from other languages, like Greek or Latin. An example of a Greek root is *mono* (one). Latin roots include *bi* (two) and *tri* (three).

A. Fill in the missing parts to make the word in bold.

1. A **monoplane** has only one set of wings.

   _____ + plane = monoplane

2. Ed is giving his old **tricycle** to his younger sister.

   _____ + _____ = tricycle

3. A **triangle** has three sides.

   _____ + _____ = triangle

4. The Rocktown newsletter is sent out **biweekly** every other Saturday.

   _____ + _____ = _____

5. Jan saved her money to buy a new **bicycle**.

   _____ + _____ = _____

**B. Write two sentences. Use the word *bicycle* in one sentence.
Use the word *triangle* in the other.**

1. _____

   _____

2. _____

   _____

Name _____

surrounded   secure   concluded   scuttle   eerie

A. Vocabulary Words: Cloze Sentences Use the correct word from above to complete each sentence.

1. In the woods, we were _____ by trees.

2. After reading a lot about birds, I _____ that they are smart.

3. Terry had an _____ feeling when she entered the old house.

4. To keep the sail _____, we had to tie many knots in the rope.

5. When the rain started, Todd had to _____ into the building.

B. Vocabulary Strategy: Dictionary Use this dictionary entry to answer the questions that follow.

1. Write a sentence using any definition of the word *right*. Have someone figure out which definition you used.

   _____

   _____

2. What is the part of speech for the second definition of *right*?

   _____

3. Write the definition used in this sentence: "The exit is on your right."

   _____

   _____

right (rīt) 1. *n.* the side or direction that is the opposite of the left
Keep to the right as you drive on the highway.

2. *n.* a claim or privilege
After you turn 18, you will have the right to vote.

3. *adj.* good or proper
You did the right thing when you helped your friend.

4. *adj.* correct or true
Who knows the right answer to this math problem?

As you reread "An Outdoor Adventure," fill in the Judgment Chart.

Action	→	Judgment
	→	
	→	
	→	
	→	

Read the passage. Then complete the questions.

Scuttling in the Night

Justin and his dad were camping out on the south rim of the Grand Canyon. They arrived and secured their tent to the ground. The canyon was beautiful and the sunset was amazing.

But now, surrounded by eerie hills that cast shadows as night fell, Justin felt differently about his surroundings. His dad didn't seem to notice the sounds of things scuttling around the way Justin did.

"Dad," he began in quiet monotone. "What are those strange noises?"

His dad turned to face him. "Let's go take a look." On the ground, a chipmunk was gathering nuts from his dad's backpack! Justin concluded that it would be a good idea to pack food supplies better next time!

1. Circle words that contain the *ou* sound.

2. Put a box around the word that has the Greek root *mono*.

3. What is an action in the passage that you can make a judgment about?

_____

_____

4. What judgment can you make about that action?

_____

5. You must _____ outdoor items before a storm.

secure   paint   stack

At Home: Reread the passage and talk about the most exciting part about camping and the least exciting part about camping.

Read the passage. Then complete the questions.

The Monster in Mabel's Kingdom

This is the first event in the passage.

A big monster came to bother Princess Mabel's kingdom. The monster stomped around to make noise. Mabel gave all the people earplugs. So the monster got angry. It rested its head in the middle of Main Street! No carts could pass by. The knights could not move the nasty monster.

Then Princess Mabel had an idea. She took her biggest feather pillow and tore it open. Feathers went up the monster's nose and under his arms, tickling him. He sneezed and giggled all the way out of town. In the end, the citizens were so happy that the monster was gone. So, they decided to make a beautiful new pillow for Princess Mabel.

1. Underline the following signal words or phrases in the passage:
   so   then   in the end

2. Put a box around the last event.

3. Now list the sequence of events in the second paragraph.

_____

_____

_____

_____

_____

Read the passage. Then complete the questions.

The Best Campfire Scare

Three sisters sat around a campfire. There was a cloudless, bright sky above. Melissa tucked her brown hair behind her ears and began her scary story.

This sentence tells an action in the story.

"Long ago, in a little town, a crowd of people saw a monster by a lake. He came back each Halloween. He sounded like this!" She howled loudly.

Suddenly, they heard noises in the forest. A monster appeared! The girls all screamed and hugged.

The monster stopped in front of them. It took off its mask and said, "It's only me, your mother. You should be proud! I had the best scare of all!"

1. Underline the actions in the story.

2. Select one action you could make a judgment about and write it on the lines.

   _____

   _____

3. Now write a judgment you can make about that action on the lines.

   _____

   _____

   _____

Name _____

Sometimes two letters stand together and make one sound. For example, the letters *sh* make one sound in the word *show*.

A. Underline the digraphs in the words below.

graph   birth   thorns   shell   think

photo   wash   when   throat   whisper

B. Read the clues. Then use the words to complete the sentences.

Across

1. Roses have sharp __.

2. I found this __ on the beach.

3. I need a drink because my __ is dry.

4. __ your hands before dinner.

5. __ can we go to the park?

Down

1. She gave __ to a baby boy.

2. Please __, the child is asleep.

3. If you __ about it, you will remember where you left your shoes.

4. To show the data, make a bar or a line __.

5. Mom always insists on taking a family __.

Name _____

A. As you read, pay attention to word accuracy.

	Many people were bullied when they were children. If they
10	weren't then it's likely that they witnessed others being bullied. It is
22	often a big problem in schools.
28	Why do bullies tease and hurt others? There are many reasons.
39	Bullies thrive on attention. A bully might refuse to take turns or
51	share toys with other children. A bully might push or shove another
63	child or shut someone out of a game. Sometimes, an unkind phrase
75	might be all it takes to hurt someone.
83	You can't always just ignore what a bully does. If you do, the
96	attacks might become more vicious. Some bullies don't believe they
106	are hurting others with their actions. They think only about how
117	they feel. They get a thrill from telling others what to do. 129

B. Read these words to yourself. Then have your partner time you. Do it two more times to see if you can beat your score!

birth	bath	when	apple	sound
photo	phony	throw	better	fowl
shell	while	shout	bagel	cloud
thorn	phrase	graph	broken	howl
shy	think	whirl	wooden	owl

Record Your Scores

Time 1: _____   Time 2: _____   Time 3: _____

© Macmillan/McGraw-Hill

At Home: Reread the passage several times to a family member and talk about what is wrong about bullying.

Name _____

The endings *-ous*, *-eous,* and *-ious* are found in words that are used to describe something. Examples are *delicious* and *poisonous*.

A. Combine the puzzle pieces to make a word.

Example: | ous | joy | _joyous_

1. ous   humor   _____

2. ious   ser   _____

3. ous   danger   _____

4. eous   gorg   _____

5. ous   nerv   _____

B. Use the correct words from above to complete each sentence.

6. The orange and pink sunset was a truly _____ sight.

7. Riding your bike without a helmet is _____.

8. I am _____ about making the speech in front of the entire school.

9. When my dad is mad, he uses a very _____ tone of voice.

10. The comedy show was very _____.

Name _____

A. Vocabulary Words Check *true* or *false* for each statement.

1. You can **thrive** at baseball when you are sleeping. ☐ true ☐ false

2. If you see a crime, you are a **witness**. ☐ true ☐ false

3. A car should come to a **halt** at a red light. ☐ true ☐ false

4. A friend who **gestures** at you is ignoring you. ☐ true ☐ false

5. An **anxious** person is calm, cool, and relaxed. ☐ true ☐ false

B. Vocabulary Strategy: Context Clues Underline the context clues that help you figure out each of the vocabulary words.

If you **witness** a crime, you should **halt**. Stopping and telling the police exactly what you saw is important. Try to stay calm. Do not get overly nervous. It is easier to make a report when you are not **anxious**. You will be better able to give a good account of what happened. Sometimes even small details like a simple movement of the hand, or a hand **gesture**, matter. This information helps police **thrive**. They may succeed in solving the crime because of your help!

Use the correct vocabulary word from above to complete each sentence.

1. When you are skilled at something, you _____ at it.

2. If you do not want to yell over the crowd, just _____ to me.

3. Jimmy was _____ about starring in his first big role.

4. Susan saw everything that happened, so she is the best _____.

5. The traffic guard yelled "_____!" to the cars, because people were still crossing the street.

© Macmillan/McGraw-Hill

Name _____

Use the Persuasion Chart to list examples of persuasive techniques the author uses in "The Truth About Bullies."

Word or Phrase	Technique

Name _____

Read the passage. Then complete the questions.

Why do Bullies Bully?

Bullies can hurt in many ways. They can use hideous gestures or words. They might ignore someone or make rude phone calls to a kid's home.

Why do bullies do these inappropriate things? Some bullies think they're being humorous. Some bullies are envious of the attention others get. They thrive on attention by showing off in front of witnesses. They think it shows strength. But being strong is not the same as being mean.

Some bullies have been teased or hurt by other kids. Sometimes their own family members bullied them! Though they might have been hurt, afraid, and anxious when they were bullied, sometimes they can't halt their own actions.

1. Underline words with digraphs *ph*, *th*, *wh*, and *sh*.

2. Circle words with *-ous*, *-ious*, or *-eous*.

3. What words does the author use to describe bullies?

_____

4. What does the author do to persuade the reader to not judge bullies?

_____

5. Joe was a _____ to the robbery at the store.
    gesture   witness   thrive

At Home: Reread the passage to a friend and talk about how you can prevent bullying.

Name _____

Each vowel can make more than one sound. Examples include
pet and *me*; *go* and *got*.

**A. Draw a line under the word that best completes each sentence.
Write the word on the line.**

1. When someone else is speaking, you should not _____.
     behave   interrupt   overwork

2. It is cool in the shade, but it is hot in the _____.
     unheated   hardboiled   sunlight

3. Miss Perkins has long arms, long legs, and even long _____!
     fingernails   baseball   afternoon

4. Will you go on the swings with me at the _____?
     underneath   basement   playground

5. Richie kept a list of places he wanted to visit in his _____.
     powder   pencilcase   notebook

6. Maisy wore a ring with her _____ in it.
     cookbook   birthstone   bathtub

7. I keep my books on shelves in my _____.
     bookcase   bathrobe   headline

8. When Uncle Doug introduces himself he has a very strong

   _____.
   downhill   handshake   feeback

**B. In the answer choices above, circle the words that have long vowel
sounds.**

A. Have a partner time you as you read the passage. Record your scores below.

	The first hot-air balloon was made by two French brothers.
10	They got their idea from watching a fire. First they made a huge bag
24	of paper and silk. Then, they placed a fire under the opening. Soon,
37	the bag filled with hot air. They were able to launch it into the sky!
52	But once the air cooled, it fell back to the ground.
63	The brothers wanted to fly just like the bag did, but they needed
76	permission. So, the brothers got permission from the king of France.
87	First they sent up a rooster, a duck, and a sheep. They wanted to
101	show the king that flying was safe. Once the king saw that the
114	animals could breathe way up high, he allowed the men to try. 126

Record Your Scores

First Read: Words Read _____   Time _____

Second Read: Words Read _____   Time _____

B. Partners Use this chart to check your partner's reading.

Speed	☐ too slow	☐ too fast	☐ just right
Paid attention to periods, commas, end punctuation	☐ never	☐ sometimes	☐ always
Accuracy	☐ skipped words	☐ self-corrected	☐ read every word
Read with feeling	☐ never	☐ sometimes	☐ always

© Macmillan/McGraw-Hill

At Home: Reread the passage with a family member and talk about what makes hot-air balloons work.

Name _____

Prefixes and suffixes are often added to a root word to change its meaning. They can help you understand the meaning of the word.

A. Which word has a prefix or a suffix? Write the word and show the prefix or suffix.

Example: unhappy   uncle   ___un/happy___

1. quickly   blackboard   _____

2. ponytail   misread   _____

3. incomplete   nowhere   _____

4. headphones   replace   _____

5. smallest   winter   _____

B. Fill in the blanks with the word from above that makes sense.

6. I was late, so I ran very _____.

7. Curt tried to _____ his frown with a smile.

8. The sign said 7 A.M., but I _____ it as saying 7 P.M.

9. The worksheet was _____ so she lost points on it.

10. Mindy was the _____ girl in the class, so she went on top of the pyramid.

permission   tended   launch   visible   expedition   solo

A. Vocabulary Words Check *yes* or *no* for each question.

1. Is it polite to ask **permission**? ☐ yes ☐ no

2. If you have not **tended** to houseplants, will they grow? ☐ yes ☐ no

3. If you **launch** a plane, will it begin its flight? ☐ yes ☐ no

4. Can a telescope make something more **visible**? ☐ yes ☐ no

5. Can an **expedition** take place in a jungle? ☐ yes ☐ no

6. Will a **solo** singer sound like three voices combined? ☐ yes ☐ no

B. Vocabulary Strategy: Greek Roots Write the letter of the word on the right that matches the meaning on the left.

1. spelled the way it sounds ____   **a.** thermostat

2. a storm shaped like a round funnel ____   **b.** cycle

3. a device that controls heat ____   **c.** telephone

4. a device that transports sounds ____   **d.** cyclone

5. an event that is repeated (goes in a circle) ____   **e.** phonetic

Name _____

As you reread the first page of "Up, Up, and Away!!!" try to find the generalization that the French brothers made. Then fill in the Generalizations Chart.

Information from Text	
Prior Knowledge	
Generalization	

© Macmillan/McGraw-Hill

Read the passage. Then complete the questions.

The Famous Flight Across the Atlantic

In 1978, everyone rushed to photograph a gas-powered balloon as it became visible just above Paris. No balloon had ever flown from the United States to France before!

Maxie Anderson and Ben Abruzzo were friends. Ben and Maxie were both daring pilots who tended to like adventure. Maxie wanted to try the expedition solo, but his wife did not give him permission. So Ben went with him. In 1977, they tried to make the 5000-kilometer expedition. It failed. But like most daring pilots, they didn't give up. They launched again in 1978. This time the friends succeeded and made history!

1. Underline three words in the last sentence that have long vowel sounds.

2. Circle the words that have prefixes and suffixes.

3. What word in the second paragraph lets you know that the author is going to make a generalization?

   _____

4. Look back at your answer to question 3. What generalization does that word help you make?

   _____

5. If I save a drowning boy, I am _____.

   daring   solo   tended

At Home: Reread the passage with an adult and talk about the daring expedition that Maxie and Ben went on together.

The same vowel can sound long or short. Make sure to notice if a vowel sounds long, like the *a* in *bake*, or short, like the *a* in *back*.

A. Draw a line under the word that best completes each sentence. Write the word on the line.

1. Tina gave her teacher an _____.
apple   anthill   airplane

2. Bakers use _____ to make bread.
shine   wheat   raincoat

3. My favorite fruits taste _____.
swim   bone   sweet

4. Jake wore a _____ when he painted to protect his shirt.
game   smock   chat

5. Lois _____ working as a newspaper carrier.
flowed   paid   stopped

6. When the sky is full of clouds and we can't see the sun then it is called _____.
overcast   outside   outrage

7. Aaron wore his yellow _____ to play outside in the rain.
raindrop   raincoat   rainbow

8. Ellie loved swimming in the ocean but she didn't like when _____ got stuck on her feet.
seashore   seafood   seaweed

B. Go back and circle the answer choices with long vowels in them.

A. Use this passage for a choral reading or Readers Theater.

Mary Elaine's Logbook on the *Alvin*

06	**February 5**
08	My name is Mary Elaine Stafford. This is my first logbook entry.
20	I've been part of this expedition for one week. I hope to find many
34	things to study.
37	**February 6**
38	Today we found a shipwreck. The damage was extensive and we
50	decided to investigate. It seems the wreck has been in place for a few
64	hundred years!
66	**February 8**
68	We just saw a cookie-cutter shark! In this part of the ocean, they are
82	extremely rare. They can tear neat wounds in the flesh of other fish.
95	**February 10**
97	We found fragments of a coral reef that had been broken up by
110	a recent hurricane. It's sad how natural disasters can destroy such
121	beautiful sea life. I hope tomorrow I see something that isn't destroyed
133	and is still in good condition. 139

**B. Read these silly sentences aloud. Pause when you see (/) and
stop when you see (//). Change your voice when you read a question mark (?)
or an exclamation point (!).**

1. Scram/ ram!// You shouldn't eat/ my ham!//

2. Did Jim/ skin his shin/ by climbing on a limb?//

3. The cat sat/ on a mat/ until she ran/ into a rat.//

4. We gave/ a standing hand/ to the band/ on the sand.//

5. Jake?// Will you shake/ that rake/ and bake a cake?//

At Home: Reread the passage, then make up silly
sentences with a family member and read them aloud.

Name _____

> Words with many syllables often have prefixes and suffixes.
> Prefixes and suffixes may change a word's meaning.

A. Circle the word that has a prefix or suffix. Then, write the word on the line with slashes between the syllables.

Example: unlike   beyond   _____un/like_____

1. incorrect   backbone   _____

2. applesauce   enormous   _____

3. lesson   misbehaving   _____

4. pleasant   calendar   _____

5. education   balloon   _____

B. Fill in the blanks with the word from above that makes sense.

6. Mike studies a lot because he cares about his _____.

7. I thought your answer was _____, but you were right!

8. The smell of fresh flowers is very _____.

9. That mountain is not just large. It's _____!

10. My sister was _____ so she was grounded for a week.

Name _____

investigate   chemicals   energy   snatching   damage   request

A. Vocabulary Words Check *true* or *false* for each statement.

1. **Snatching** food from a friend is a nice thing to do. ☐ true ☐ false

2. One way to **investigate** is to ask questions. ☐ true ☐ false

3. It is dangerous to mix **chemicals**. ☐ true ☐ false

4. Most people would be happy about car **damage**. ☐ true ☐ false

5. When I **request** an apple, I give you an apple. ☐ true ☐ false

B. Vocabulary Strategy: Word Families Draw a line from the word on the left to the word on the right that is in the same word family.

1. user   **a.** furious

2. impossible   **b.** misuse

3. confused   **c.** attendant

4. attended   **d.** confusion

5. fury   **e.** possibly

Name _____

Read "Alvin: Underwater Exploration," again, and write the events of
the story in the Sequence Chart.

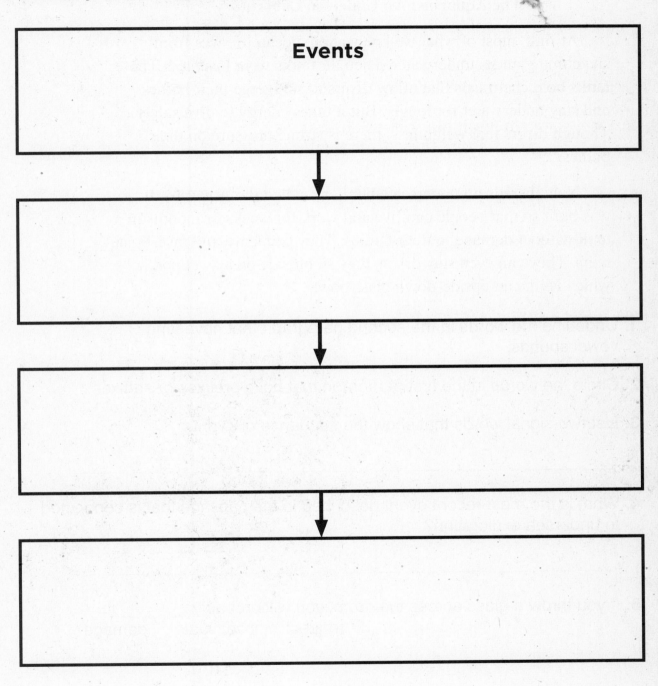

Events

Read the passage. Then complete the questions.

The Aquarius: An Undersea Laboratory

At first, most of what we knew about ocean life was from snatching glances underwater. Then air tanks were invented. These tanks hold chemicals that allow divers to submerge their bodies and stay underwater for longer. But it takes energy to dive safely. Though divers feel weightless, there is strong pressure on their bodies.

Now there is an undersea laboratory called the Aquarius. It was built so that people can live and work for weeks or months in a tank without damage to their bodies. They can leave and investigate reefs. They can even stay dry as they sit outside on a "wet porch," which is like an upside-down glass bowl.

1. Underline the words in the second paragraph that have long vowel sounds.

2. Circle the words in the first paragraph that have prefixes or suffixes.

3. List two signal words that show the sequence of events.

_____

4. What is the most recent event described in the passage that is connected to undersea exploration?

_____

5. If you throw a glass across the room, you will probably _____ it.

                    request   investigate   damage

© Macmillan/McGraw-Hill

At Home: Reread the passage with a family member and talk about the sequence of events of your day.

Name _____

Read the passage. Then complete the questions.

Big Brothers and Big Sisters

Big Brothers and Big Sisters groups help many children. When kids are faced with difficult choices, they need someone to talk to. Many kids need a mentor, or someone they can trust.

A teacher might see a child who needs a mentor. Then the teacher will contact a Big Brother or Big Sister. At the school, the child and mentor will get to know one another. Then they might talk on the phone, see a show, or even visit a zoo! Just having someone to chat with is often all these kids need. When you get older, you should consider being a Big Brother or Big Sister!

1. Circle the following signal words in the passage:
   many   just   should

2. Underline sentences that show persuasive techniques.

3. Write what you think the writer is trying to persuade the reader to do.

_____

_____

_____

_____

Name _____

Read the passage. Then complete the questions.

Gas-Powered Balloons

At first, many hot-air balloons were not
very safe. The fire to heat the balloons could
burn the fabric above it. Also, most hot-air
balloons were not strong enough to fly for
a long period of time. People quickly found
that putting a gas that is lighter than air into
a balloon could work better.

Gas balloons came with their own dangers,
though. Often, if the gases mixed with air, a fire
could start.

However, many gas balloons are still visible in the skies today.
During a large sporting event, you might see a blimp filled with
helium gas in the clouds above.

1. Put a box around the following signal words in the passage:
   many   most   often

2. Underline the generalizations in the passage.

3. Now write your own generalization about hot air balloons on
   the lines.

   _____

   _____

   _____

Name _____

Read the passage. Then complete the questions.

Becoming an Astronaut

Before you become an astronaut you must learn a lot of different things. First, you need to know a lot about science or engineering.

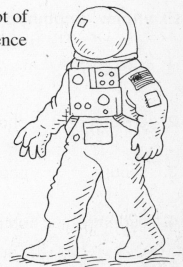

Next, an astronaut in training should know other languages and about other cultures. Astronauts can come from different countries and you will need to be able to work closely with these people up in space.

Then you will need to learn to fly a plane and a shuttle. That is, if you want to pilot the space ship one day. After passing many other tests and meeting many requirements you will finally, be ready for space!

1. Underline the following signal words in the passage:
   first   next   then   finally

2. Put a box around the first thing that you must do to become an astronaut.

3. Now find two things that an astronaut must learn to do after that. Write your answer on the lines:

   _____

   _____

A. **Which word has a prefix or suffix? Write the word and circle the prefix or suffix.**

Example: unpinned   seasick   ___(un)pinned___

1. servant   surround   _____

2. curious   phonics   _____

3. secure   impressed   _____

4. birdbath   outrageous   _____

5. tremble   assistant   _____

B. **Use the correct word from above to complete each sentence.**

1. Miss Blatt's classroom _____ this week is Phil.

2. Aren't you _____ by the wonderful project that we made?

3. In the story, the _____ prepared dinner for the rich family.

4. I think that store's high prices are _____!

5. Josh was _____ about what was in the box, so he ripped it open quickly.